HEALTH & SOCIAL WELFARE

Challenging Ideas in Mental Health

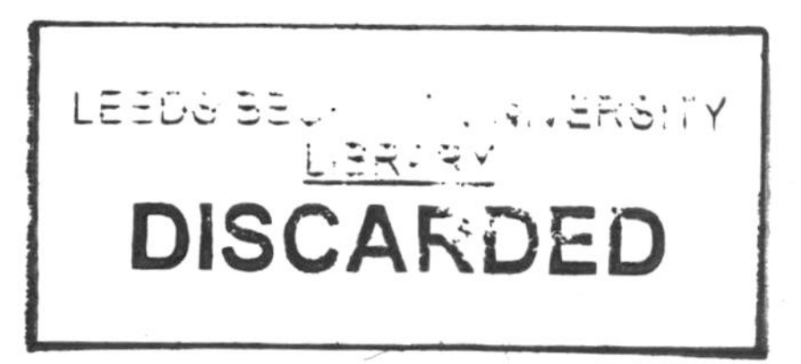

Module 1
Shifting Boundaries

For information on related Open University courses and study packs write to the Information Assistant, School of Health and Social Welfare, The Open University, Walton Hall, Milton Keynes MK7 6AA, tel. 01908 653743, or visit http://www.open.ac.uk/shsw

Alternatively, you may visit the main Open University website at http://www.open.ac.uk where you can learn more about the wide range of courses and packs offered at all levels by The Open University.

To purchase a selection of Open University course materials visit the webshop at www.ouw.co.uk, or contact Open University Worldwide, Michael Young Building, Walton Hall, Milton Keynes MK7 6AA, United Kingdom for a brochure. Tel. +44 (0)1908 858785; fax +44 (0)1908 858787; e-mail ouwenq@open.ac.uk

The Open University, Walton Hall, Milton Keynes MK7 6AA

First published 2004

Edited, designed and typeset by The Open University

Printed in the United Kingdom by Hobbs the Printers Limited, Brunel Road, Totton, Hampshire SO40 3WX

ISBN 0 7492 6867 0

1.1

Contents

Introduction to Module 1

Learning outcomes

After studying this module you should be able to:

- recognise the significance of a holistic perspective for mental health and distress
- identify dilemmas and challenges for people involved with mental health services as workers and service users
- apply the concept of boundaries to explanations of mental health and distress
- explain the impact of ethnicity and discrimination on mental health and distress
- assess the relationships between mind, body and brain
- discuss the concept of citizenship in relation to the boundaries of exclusion and inclusion for service users/survivors.

Welcome to the first module of *Challenging Ideas in Mental Health*. The world of mental health and distress is complex, exciting and full of diverse views and opinions. It is a world of intense emotion and experience, of power and powerlessness and of inclusion and exclusion. In one way or another we all have a place in this world: we all experience degrees of mental health and distress as we journey through our lives. Some people come into contact with mental health services in periods of distress; others work in health or social care settings that provide mental health services. You may have family members, friends or colleagues who experience periods of distress. You may have similar experiences yourself. Even people who do not have direct contact with individuals who experience distress or with services confront the public image of mental health and distress in the media, in contexts as diverse as soap operas and news reports.

So, mental health and distress affect us all. Unit 1 *Boundaries of Explanation* explores boundaries within and between groups, within and between explanatory frameworks and within and between experiences of mental health and distress. It looks at boundaries that appear fixed alongside those that change and shift over time, and it also introduces the holistic model used in the course.

In Unit 2 *A Holistic Approach: Hilary's Story* you explore the holistic model of understanding that underpins the course. Using this model you consider aspects of mental health and distress through a range of experiences and dimensions of experience – social, emotional, physical, psychological and spiritual (personal meaning). Each of these dimensions will be introduced, and the relationships and boundaries between them discussed, in relation to one woman's experiences of depression.

Within certain boundaries there may be clearly defined roles that govern the ways people interact and relate. At other times the boundaries may be blurred and roles less clear-cut. Relationships between people who use (and survive) services, between service users/survivors and workers, and between the personal and professional lives of workers are explored in Unit 3 *Relationship Boundaries*. This unit uses the example of continuous observation, whereby people detained in hospital are constantly watched by staff, often within arm's length, to explore the challenges posed to professional and personal boundaries.

Certain boundaries are defined or formed in different ways within different cultures and across national borders. In Unit 4 *Culture, Ethnicity and Mental Health* mental health and distress in relation to diverse societies are critically discussed and international aspects of mental health and services are examined. In this unit you are also introduced to the concept of cultural competence and the practice implications of the approach.

Unit 5 *Relating Mind and Body* starts by exploring how life experiences are felt and known in the physical body and explores the relationship between the mind, body and brain. Examples are drawn from brain injury and ME which challenge the boundaries between physical and mental health, often known as the mind/body split.

The final unit in this module, Unit 6 *Boundaries of Exclusion*, considers the concepts of exclusion and inclusion and the rewards and challenges of citizenship. The involvement and employment of service users/survivors are used to illustrate the boundaries of social exclusion and the possibilities for inclusion.

Unit 1 Boundaries of Explanation

Contents

You will need:

Resources:

Reading 1 'Madness, distress and the language of inclusion'

Reading 2 'Terms of engagement'

The video 'A quiet night on Roundhay Wing'

Learning outcomes

After studying this unit you should be able to:

1. reflect on the concept of 'boundaries' and its relevance to mental health and distress
2. discuss language and terminology in relation to mental health and distress
3. appreciate different ways of viewing mental distress
4. compare the medical and social models of mental distress
5. understand and describe the holistic model.

1 Introduction

This unit looks at what we are calling 'boundaries of explanation'. It tackles key issues such as:

- What are mental health and distress – and who decides?
- What are the views of people who have acquired a label of 'mental illness'?
- What are the views of those who determine – and patrol – the boundary between mental distress and 'normality'?

The unit looks at language and terminology and the differences between people. It looks at medical and social models, and their competing claims, and introduces a holistic model which embraces key aspects of both approaches.

2 Boundaries of exclusion

The first idea to come under critical consideration is that of boundaries. Boundaries can be helpful and, indeed, we use them here as a means of exploring different, and competing, explanations of mental health and distress. However, they can also be limiting and excluding, emphasising the differences between people, some of which run very deep. At their simplest, boundaries put limits on tasks so that they appear manageable. They help to mark out personal space in a shared office, or indicate the extent of someone's home and garden. Boundaries are often physical, represented by partitions or walls or fences, to show who is allowed in and who is not (and under what terms).

The sorts of boundaries we consider here are more *social* than physical. They also define 'who's in and who's out', as Shakespeare's King Lear explains:

> *So we'll live,*
> *And pray, and sing, and tell old tales, and laugh*
> *At gilded butterflies, and hear poor rogues*
> *Talk of court news; and we'll talk with them too –*
> *Who loses and who wins; who's in, who's out –*
> *And take upon's the mystery of things ...*

(King Lear, Act V, Scene iii, lines 11–16)

The king at this point was excluded from the royal court and was more at one with the 'poor rogues' on the outside. This was because he had crossed a social divide – into madness. He was on the other side of a crucial social boundary that determines 'who's out' on account of their mental distress. In many ways, social boundaries are the most pervasive. They serve to exclude people who look or behave differently, and they are much harder to shift than a garden fence.

2.1 Boundaries and terminology

In another context Shakespeare asked, 'What's in a name?', and suggested by way of an answer that a rose may smell as sweet whatever it is called. In the context of social boundaries, however, the language used is actually very important in determining 'who's in' and 'who's out'.

Activity 1.1 **Looking at language**

30 minutes

Learning outcomes 1 and 2

What is the language of mental distress? Who are the people who experience it?

Make a list of all the words you can think of (in past as well as present usage, and including colloquial and slang words) that describe the condition or experience. Then list the words used to refer to the people who have the condition or experience, again including slang terms.

Then return to the articles by Rachel Perkins and Diana Rose (Readings 1 and 2) that you were asked to read in the Introduction and Study Guide. Read them through again, and write a short summary of the authors' views on language and terminology.

Comment Your list probably contained some or all of the following terms: lunacy, mania, madness, insanity, mental ill health, mental illness, mental distress, mental health problems. More specifically, you may have mentioned schizophrenia, depression, anxiety, neurosis, psychopathology and paranoia. One of the course testers suggested possession and witchcraft.

Your list of names for the people concerned probably contained some or all of the following: lunatic, madman/woman, mentally ill person and mental patient, as well as slang terms such as loony, nutter, psycho, schizo and weirdo. Course testers added: mental, maniac, barking, loopy, touched, unhinged and highly strung. In addition, there are the names adopted by people on the receiving end of the terminology and services, such as users, clients and survivors. Some of these terms are combined to become mental health service users/survivors.

The two authors are themselves users of mental health services as well as being involved in mental health research and practice. Perkins dismisses the word 'distress' as being too inclusive. Her argument is that everyone experiences distress but not everyone experiences 'madness', and to claim they do is to diminish and trivialise the latter experience. She suggests that service users should 'embrace mad pride' and celebrate their differences. Rose accepts that some service users regard their experience as an illness that can be treated. She argues, however, in favour of the term 'mental distress'. At the same time, she suggests that this should be linked with a more positive outlook that includes valuing and learning from that experience, and connecting it with 'the discourse of rights'.

What are we to make of this? One conclusion to be drawn is that there are no easy answers to the question of what terminology to use, nor any ready-to-use terms that are acceptable to everyone. However, the course aims to draw on these accounts – and the accounts of others – to use language that is acceptable and meaningful. This probably means using 'mental distress', but not in a way that demeans or trivialises. Instead, it means taking a positive stand – celebrating difference and diversity, valuing people's experiences of mental distress and supporting their rights, especially their right to be included in the mainstream of society.

2.2 Boundaries of difference

One of the things that language does is define and give a name to differences between people – to delineate the boundaries that separate them. In the mental health field, the 'mad' are at one end of the social divide that separates the 'normal' from the 'abnormal'. They are 'the other', a point made in the article by Perkins: 'To be mad is to be defined as "other"'.

This is a recurring theme in the mental health field. In the following passage Abina Parshad-Griffin, Chair of the Mental Health Action Group for the Disability Rights Commission (DRC), reflects on 'otherness' and what it means to be 'the other':

> I could use different aspects of who I am that make the whole of me, as a kind of through-the-looking-glass. And I can give an example: being mixed race, if I had to fill in different forms in various countries, I'd have to tick different boxes. So in South Africa, I would have been 'coloured'. In America, I would be 'black' because one drop of Black blood makes you 'black', and excluded. In South America, I could possibly be 'mixed race', or I could even pass for 'white' when you have the hierarchy of colour coding. But guess what I'm called in England or the UK? 'Other'. And it's that otherness that is part of my identity, and I believe that mental health discrimination is that otherness which is sometimes indefinable. But you pick it up – this overt and covert discrimination. I call it 'psychophobia': fear of mental illness. And there are certain conditions. Like somebody asks me, 'What do you do?' And I say, 'Schizophrenia.' You know that's going to be a conversation-stopper and you will also know that it's going to be associated with violence, with antisocial behaviour, which is not at all the case. That's rare.
>
> (Disability Rights Commission, taped conversation, n.d.)

To be 'other', in many instances, is to be on the wrong side of the boundary. The fact that Parshad-Griffin is mixed race gives her an officially designated category of 'other' in the UK. In addition, of course, her experience of mental distress reinforces her 'otherness'. To be regarded as 'other' is to be treated differently, which often means prejudice and discrimination. 'Otherness' comes into play at all levels, but especially, it seems, when mental distress triggers 'psychophobia' in the people around. Although Parshad-Griffin's situation also features 'double discrimination' (Baxter *et al.*, 1990) because of her mixed race designation, in many ways it is typical of the experiences of people who have periods of mental distress. Psychophobia leads to prejudice and discrimination. This may be something you have experienced yourself or have witnessed in others.

The point of creating 'others' or a 'them', according to Harper (2002a, p. 8), is that it projects problems on to other people so that we 'get to see ourselves as normal'. May (2000) suggests that the 'us' and 'them' ideas that are prevalent in the mental health services should be challenged: 'Such ideas assume that there are "ill" people and there are "well" people, and an uncrossable void exists between them' (p. 25).

Being seen as someone with mental health problems may result in discrimination, often of a severe kind, as many people have found to their cost. The experience of being on the 'other' side of the mental health/distress boundary may be accompanied by unemployment, breakdown of relationships, low income and poor housing.

Activity 1.2 **A quiet night on Roundhay Wing**

1 hour Learning outcomes 1 and 2

You should now watch the video, 'A quiet night on Roundhay Wing'. This is a story of people who have been designated as 'other' and confined to the psychiatric wing of St James's Hospital in Leeds. Watch it right through first and then make some notes. You will be asked to watch it again in Unit 24, the final unit of the course.

The film was scripted and acted by mental health service users/survivors. It is hard-hitting, especially in its references to the people and practices that have dominated – and defined – their lives, often over many years. It is a true story in the sense that it is grounded in and reflects people's real experiences, but the events portrayed did not actually take place.

Watch the film now. When you write your notes afterwards, you may find it helpful to divide them into:

- your *reactions* to what you saw and heard; in other words, what you felt as you watched it
- your *reflections* on the key messages: what you thought after the film had ended.

Comment This a thought-provoking play. It aroused a mixture of reactions in the course team when we watched it together. It is easy to identify with the people who are the 'others' in society's terms, but it may be harder to accept their views of those they regard as their oppressors and gaolers. Doctors, nurses, hospitals, day centres and drug companies all come in for criticism. Whatever your views, record them fully now.

This is your 'benchmark', a record of where you stand at the beginning of the course. Although you may decide to watch the video as a whole or in parts as you work through subsequent units, you engage with it fully again in Unit 24. At that point, we invite you to watch it right through and revisit the notes you have just made, with a view to seeing where you stand in relation to this benchmark. You will also have the chance to listen to an audio recording of mental health service users/survivors and mental health workers and professionals talking about the video after they have watched it together. This will give you the opportunity to compare your reactions and reflections with theirs.

2.3 Boundaries of 'normality'

The origin of the 'other' in society is the widespread human tendency to create categories where people who don't fit in can be placed away from the mainstream. Social categories may lead to prejudice and discrimination, but may also lead to the physical separation of people to the margins of that society. Sibley (1995) traces the physical marginalisation of people in what he calls the 'geographies of exclusion'. Part of the process of exclusion is where the 'bad', the 'mad' and the 'imperfect' are deemed to be 'other' and, often in stereotyped form, are disregarded or rejected.

Being the 'other' in mental health terms means being on the 'them' side of the normality/abnormality boundary. What does it mean to be regarded as abnormal? Indeed, what is the nature of mental distress? What does it mean to have mental health problems? It all depends on where the boundaries are drawn, and by whom. A boundary may often be drawn, for example, in a way that differentiates mental distress from ideas of what constitutes mental health and wellbeing. A person experiencing mental distress is, therefore, at least temporarily on the other side of the divide from those who are 'normal' or 'sane'. Boundaries divide and define, but do they help to explain?

A recent definition of mental disorder states that '"Mental disorder" means any disability or disorder of mind or brain which results in an impairment or disturbance of mental functioning; and "mentally disordered" is to be read accordingly' (Department of Health, 2002, p. 3).

So that's clear, then. Or is it? The concept of disorder suggests its counterpart – that there is some sort of mental 'order', an internal state where there is calm and coherence. The boundary between mental health and mental disorder is also concerned with the controversial idea of normality and what society regards as normal (Coppock and Hopton, 2000). It may be more helpful, in human terms, to think of a continuum of mental health and distress. Instead of being on one side of a social divide or the other, we are at varying points on the continuum and can move along it, back and forth, stopping and (re)starting as life changes. This is a more inclusive way of thinking about mental distress, avoiding the fixed boundary between 'them' and 'us', and allowing everyone to move between points as circumstances change and episodes of distress come and go.

This is not a view shared by everyone. In the article you read earlier by Rachel Perkins, she argues against the notion of a continuum on the grounds that it disguises and diminishes real differences between people. What needs to change, in her view, is the value we give to those differences. What do you think? The next activity gives you the opportunity to reflect on what 'normality' means.

Activity 1.3 **What is mental 'normality'?**

20 minutes

Learning outcomes 2 and 3

Think about what normality means to you. In what ways do you consider yourself to be normal? Note down some thoughts and, if possible, discuss your views with someone else.

Comment

It is not easy to define normality, as it differs over time and between cultures. However, there is a sense of it meaning the ordinary or everyday aspects of life. This was certainly what course testers thought when asked what normality meant to them. One said:

> Normality for me is 'everyday'. This might cover a range of emotions and feelings, from boredom and dissatisfaction to happy and engaged. Normality includes the usual, whether that be activities such as shopping, working or driving, or the uncommon but planned-for, such as going on holiday.

Another said:

> Normality means day-to-day coping and rational thoughts, an ability to look at things objectively.

By way of contrast, creative artists and inspirational leaders live at least some of their lives in ways that are not ordinary and everyday. They may not be normal in that sense. But with talents that are way beyond those of the average person, they may come to be greatly revered. Other people, on the wrong side of the divide, may fare less well. The challenges of defining normality are highlighted well by Johnstone:

> How quiet do you have to be before you can be called withdrawn? How angry is aggressive? How sudden is impulsive? How unusual is delusional? How excited is manic? How miserable is depressed? The answers are to be found not in some special measuring skill imparted during psychiatric training, but in the psychiatrist's and relatives' shared beliefs about how 'normal' people should behave.
>
> (Johnstone, 1989, p. 243)

It is interesting to think about how normality and abnormality come to be defined in society. This point is taken up by Shaw and Woodward (in press), who suggest that people are less tolerant of unhappiness. This has led to more and more medicalisation of what at other times and in other countries might be regarded as normal human distress. Another take on the pathologising of day-to-day life experiences is the (rather tongue-in-cheek) concept of happiness as an abnormal state (Bentall, 1992). It is abnormal in the sense that it is not something experienced as ordinary and everyday. There are, of course, dangers in extending the boundaries of abnormality ever further, and the absurdity of classifying happiness as 'a major affective disorder, pleasant type', for instance, is plain to see. The nature of normality is contested, and so too is the nature of mental illness or distress. In the next section, we look at competing explanations of mental distress.

3 Ways of viewing mental distress

The first point to note is that there are two key competing ways of viewing mental illness or distress: physical and social. One of the functions of this course is to draw together aspects of these accounts in order to cross the boundaries that they create and maintain. Our aim in this respect is to devise a third way, a more rounded and holistic approach that brings together the best of both worlds. In the meantime, though, the physical and social explanations predominate. Physical explanations are based on, for example, notions of brain dysfunction or genetic predisposition. Mental distress, in those terms, is a disorder of the mind, akin to a physical illness. Social explanations, on the other hand, are based on an understanding of difference and discrimination: on structural factors in society that separate people and may come to oppress them. Another way of understanding mental distress – and this links with our 'third way', the holistic (whole person) approach – is to view it from the standpoint of those who have experienced it. This is an important vantage point. The next activity invites you to read, and reflect on, the personal experiences of two women who have experienced mental distress.

Activity 1.4 **Personal experiences of mental distress**

30 minutes

Learning outcome 3

Read the two short extracts below by Jasna Russo and Veronica Dewan. Make notes on how each explains the origins of their mental distress.

> **Jasna Russo**
>
> I come from Yugoslavia, that is where I was committed to a psychiatric institution for the first time at the age of 20, just before that I was raped, and long before that I had been sexually abused by my father, therefore I became mad. Madness was revealing the abuse, therefore he committed me one more time and then I left forever and now I live somewhere else.
>
> Although these are the facts of my life, they cannot represent it because so much of who I am remains out of them. I feel like I am disappearing behind these words. Every attempt to describe myself in terms of what happened to me reduces me to a story with which I never agreed, which was never mine. My true biography is resistance to my biography. I try to live that resistance every day and it is not only about staying out of psychiatry. There are many other things in my life that I need to struggle with. Through that struggle I'm always becoming more of the person that I am, on the contrary to the one that was meant to be.
>
> (Source: Russo, 2001, pp. 36–7)

Veronica Dewan

I became engaged in an official system of care at birth, a system that denigrated my Indian heritage, a system that made meaningless my true identity. It was my first encounter with social services in 1957 at six weeks of age – an illegitimate, 'mixed race', hard-to-place baby. [...]

Several inpatient admissions to an acute psychiatric ward compounded childhood and adult experiences of racism, misunderstanding and intimidation. I persisted with suicidal plans and attempts, and was severely depressed, with psychotic episodes of manifestations of my adoptive mother's attempts to kill me as a child. The underlying requirement of the psychiatric system appeared to involve fully internalising the racism, to make me completely ill forever. [...]

As I challenge more and more my own perceptions, question their origins and try to understand my place in the world, I believe that the official care system tried to silence me into living a life that was not my own. While institutional racism continues, by its insidious nature, to cause so much unarticulated pain I have to be vigilant in holding onto my right to exist, as a Black woman of dual heritage. The people who have no interest or motive in controlling me, but only a willingness to engage through mutual love, acceptance and respect, are those who remain in my life.

(Source: Dewan, 2001, pp. 44–9)

Comment

Jasna's explanation of her mental distress includes:

- sexual abuse and rape, leading to an episode of 'madness'
- admission to hospital
- disclosure of her father's abuse
- consequent compulsory readmission to hospital
- migration from Yugoslavia
- day-to-day resistance.

Veronica's explanation includes:

- admission into care as an illegitimate, mixed race, hard-to-place baby
- childhood experiences of racism (combined with the denigration of her heritage)
- admissions to hospital
- suicide bids
- breakdown of the relationship with her adoptive mother.

The two authors acknowledge the importance of their personal experiences and histories. Abuse, rejection and separation played a part in creating their experiences of mental distress. They also highlight how their experiences of mental health systems had a negative impact on their lives, compounding their original difficulties. They have a voice now, as survivors and writers, but the systems of the time sought to silence them. Their accounts also point to structural factors within society – racism, discrimination and oppression.

Is mental distress a cry for help? Is it, as Russo suggests, a form of resistance? Or is it a response to 'unarticulated pain'? In the next section we look at models for understanding mental distress.

4 Models for understanding

Are people with mental health problems ill? Or are they disabled? The practice of psychiatry is based on the premise that people are ill and need to be treated. A contrary view is coming to the fore, however: that people with mental health problems are disabled (Disability Rights Commission, 2003). What is the difference? The notion of an illness suggests a temporary incapacity, and leaves open the possibility that it is a treatable condition. Disability, on the other hand, suggests a longer-term state of affairs. This does not mean that it is a permanent or fixed state. The disabled people's movement takes the view that people are disabled by society, not by the underlying impairment, so that disabled people can be fully part of society providing that social barriers are removed. This is the social model of disability (we return to it later in the unit). Could it apply equally to people with mental health problems? It could be argued that people experiencing mental distress are, in effect, 'disabled' by society's prejudice towards them and the discrimination they experience as a result.

Activity 1.5 **Mental illness or mental disability?**

20 minutes

Learning outcomes 3 and 4

This is an opportunity for you to reflect on the nature of the boundary between mental illness and mental disability. Do you regard someone with a mental health problem (which may include yourself or someone you live or work with) as ill or as disabled? Or do you see this person as both mentally distressed *and* disabled? What are the implications of the distinction?

Comment

There are differing views within the mental health survivor movement about where people see themselves and how they want to be treated. Diana Rose, for example, opts for medical treatment:

> I would prefer to treat my mental distress, at least partly, on the model of physical medicine as a practice, as I have experienced it at its best. This does not commit me at all to a brain-based causative model of my distress or to a definition of it as an 'illness'. It is a statement about how I would prefer to be treated. When I am in crisis they can throw the whole BNF [British National Formulary] at me – all drugs above recommended limits and serious polypharmacy.
>
> I have my own story about why I become distressed. It is not a story of therapeutic optimism – that knowing why it happens will prevent it happening again. This is just my conclusion, not a recommendation for anyone else. Its advantage is that I do not feel an utter failure each time I crack up because I have not been devoting time, energy and money to making sure it never happens again.
>
> (Rose, 2002, p. 21)

Abina Parshad-Griffin (Chair of the DRC's Mental Health Action Group) sees herself as *disabled* by her mental illness:

> we're not just people with a mental illness. I mean – in my own example – I happen to be a mixed race woman of colour, a member of the underclass with a mental health disability. And that is part and fully who I am. And what I find interesting is the way that I can look at my race from my disability and my class and my gender, and likewise I can look at my disability from the things I've learned about racism and discrimination. I think the most important thing is that those of us who feel able to embrace our disability in a positive way do so, and that the Disability Rights Commission enables us rather than disables us from doing so.
>
> (Disability Rights Commission, taped conversation, n.d.)

In Parshad-Griffin's view, she is disabled not only by her mental health problems but also by her class, gender and race. She explains her situation with reference to multiple medical and social factors. We now look, in turn, at medical and social approaches to mental health and distress.

4.1 The medical model

Although the term used in the course is mental distress, the term mental illness is probably much more familiar to lay people. This is reflected in the widely held view that people on the receiving end of mental health services are experiencing episodes of illness. It is also reflected in the branch of medicine, psychiatry, which is concerned with mental distress or illness. Psychiatrists treat patients for what they regard as specific diseases of the brain. The emphasis is on physical causes of mental distress and the focus tends to be on symptoms. Psychiatrists make diagnoses of specific types of mental disorder and on this basis they pursue a course of treatment, drawing on medication or other physical interventions to reduce or contain the symptoms. This is the medical model (or more properly the biomedical model) of mental illness. A focus solely on the treatment of symptoms may, however, be at the expense of a more rounded approach to the distress that lies underneath, a point we return to later.

The medical model is familiar because it has a relatively long history. The idea of insanity as illness was established in the 19th century, as Porter indicates:

> most nineteenth century physicians maintained that insanity was ultimately rooted in the organism, particularly in the brain; for that reason therapy needed to be incorporated within a medical model, and prescribed by physicians. There followed a dramatic increase in books on insanity, virtually all by doctors; and a growing body of 'mad-doctors' emerged, called 'alienists'.
>
> (Porter, 1999, p. 498)

The search for a biological cause of mental distress continues in biomedical research. This includes exploring people's genetic inheritance in order to establish whether or not there is a genetic predisposition to developing mental distress. Following successes in the Human Genome Project, there is, as Chadwick (2000) points out, 'an intense interest in the genetic basis of mental disorders' (p. 35). This is an approach welcomed by Perkins:

> I've a confession to make. Unpopular as such views are in many quarters, I think my mental health problems are caused by the way the chemicals in my brain – my neurotransmitters – work, and that this is part of my genetic inheritance. Now please don't think that I believe this sort of organic explanation of distress to be any 'truer' in an absolute sense than assorted cognitions, intrapsychic processes or the action of various deities. I do not. It is simply that organic/biological explanations work for me.
>
> (Perkins, 2003, p. 6)

Of course, a genetic predisposition – even if it could be established – would not in itself mean that mental distress would inevitably follow. It could, however, make people vulnerable in certain circumstances, especially when confronted by environmental risks (Rutter and Plomin, 1997). Although predominant for many years, the biomedical model is increasingly seen to have weaknesses as well as strengths. Its critics include some of the people on the receiving end as well as some of those who provide mental health services. The psychiatrists Bracken and Thomas (2000), for example, accept that medicine continues to have a role 'in helping those of us who experience episodes of madness, despair and alienation' (p. 19). At the same time, they contend that psychiatric diagnoses may oversimplify a complex reality and that by casting people's experiences in pathological terms it can be 'profoundly disempowering and stigmatising' (p. 19). One of the reasons for this could well be that diagnosis is a process of classification, creating boundaries around different 'conditions' and between the people who experience them, as well as between those who experience them and those who don't.

Activity 1.6 **A review of the biomedical model**

20 minutes Learning outcome 4

The first part of the review is to consider the *possible benefits* of the biomedical model. Make a list of them.

Then consider the *possible pitfalls* of this approach. Make a second list.

Draw on your own personal or work experience, if appropriate, but also re-read and reflect on the extracts in this unit.

Comment The *possible benefits* of the biomedical approach include:

- a tangible explanation
- a named condition that may absolve people from feeling responsible
- relief of symptoms
- access to help and support
- the possibility that mental distress is time-limited.

The *possible pitfalls* include:

- a focus on symptoms and their treatment (which may be at the expense of other approaches)
- the continuing dominance of psychiatry in mental health (and maintenance of the traditional medical hierarchy)
- locating the problem in the person
- focusing on the individual in isolation rather than in their social context
- overlooking the importance of psychological, spiritual, social and cultural factors.

Although the biomedical approach has the potential to be helpful (and many people testify to this), where it falls short, it seems, is in its relatively restricted view of mental distress. While there is acceptance, even among mental health activists, of the need for biological research, and the consideration of genetic factors, there is also the view that this is not enough (Campbell, 1999; Beresford and Hopton, 2002). Biological and genetic factors come into play, if at all, when personal, interpersonal or social factors trigger them. What is missing is the bigger picture. Attempts have been made in recent years to remedy this deficit, particularly through the development of what is called the 'biopsychosocial' model. This, as its name suggests, retains the 'bio' aspect of the biomedical approach, and considers that biological explanations are important. At the same time, however, it recognises the importance of the psychological and social origins of mental distress (Double, 2002). The importance of the social context is stressed by Bracken and Thomas:

> we will never be able to understand the various elements of our mental life such as thoughts, beliefs, feelings, and values if we think of them as located inside the brain. Trying to grasp the meaningful reality of sadness, alienation, obsession, fear, and madness by looking at scans or analysing biochemistry is like trying to understand a painting by looking at the canvas without reference to its wider world.
>
> (Bracken and Thomas, 2002, p. 1434)

The National Service Framework for Mental Health (Department of Health, 1999) similarly indicates that mental health problems are linked with a range of social factors. Examples include:

- unemployed people are twice as likely to have depression as people in work
- children in the poorest households are three times more likely to have mental health problems than children in well-off households
- half of all women and a quarter of all men will be affected by depression at some period during their lives
- people who have been abused or been victims of domestic violence have higher rates of mental health problems
- between a quarter and a half of people using night shelters or sleeping rough may have a serious mental disorder, and up to half may be alcohol dependent
- some black and minority ethnic groups are diagnosed as having higher rates of mental disorder than the general population; refugees are especially vulnerable
- there is a high rate of mental disorder in the prison population
- people with drug and alcohol problems have higher rates of other mental health problems
- people with physical illnesses have higher rates of mental health problems.

(Department of Health, 1999, p. 14)

The term 'biopsychosocial' was coined by George Engel in 1980 (Engel, 1980). The advantage of the model is that it combines the biomedical approach with the 'bigger picture' of the person's history and current relationships and networks. It is an approach that 'looks at the whole person, their life and circumstances, and not simply into their brain' (Double, 2002, p. 7). According to Pilgrim (2002), it is an approach that is both inclusive and holistic (although this is not the same as the *holistic model* that we outline later, in Section 5). We will return to the biomedical model at other points in the course; at this juncture it is timely to look at a purely *social* model for a possible explanation of mental distress.

4.2 The social model of disability

The social model of disability, as its name suggests, is drawn from outside the mental health field (and also from outside medicine). It is a formulation developed by physically disabled academics, in the first place as a reaction against the medical model which had hitherto been predominant in their lives. Subsequently, the social model was refined to become an explanation of how it is society that *disables* people, not the impairment itself. It also became a focus for campaign and action. The social model distinguishes between the physical or sensory impairment and the effect of that impairment, which includes the exclusion of disabled people from mainstream society because of the social, environmental and attitudinal barriers that serve to keep them out. The barriers include inaccessible buildings and transport, a lack of hearing loops, ramps, personal assistance, and so on. In this analysis, it is not the impairment that is disabling, but society itself (Oliver and Barnes, 1998).

Activity 1.7 **What has the social model of disability got to do with mental health?**

20 minutes Learning outcome 4

There are two parts to the question 'What has the social model of disability got to do with mental health?':

- Is mental distress a form of disability and, therefore, capable of being explained by the social model?
- Is the social model of disability relevant in any other way to mental health service users?

Write down your views. If possible, talk to someone else and share your thoughts. These are evolving ideas, so there are no hard-and-fast answers.

Comment Mental distress could be seen as a form of impairment, on a par with a physical or sensory impairment. Following this line of thought, the impairment would not be the primary concern – rather, it would be the *disabling* reactions of society generally and mental health services in particular that would be the issue. The removal of social, environmental and attitudinal barriers, according to the principles of the social model of disability, would enable people experiencing mental distress to be fully engaged in society. This, of course, leaves out a debate we touched on earlier about whether mental distress is an impairment or an episodic 'illness' that is temporary and treatable.

Reflect on this analysis. Does it make sense in relation to people and/or settings you are familiar with?

Alternatively, mental health service users/survivors could borrow from the social model of disability those aspects that are most useful. This could include the development of the biomedical model into a more biopsychosocial model by emphasising – as the social model does – the social aspects of, and the societal barriers that exist towards, their mental distress. Additionally, mental health service users/survivors could benefit from joining the wider disabled people's movement in order to push forward an agenda of human rights, supported employment, personal assistance and citizenship. (The links and benefits of a closer association are suggested by Campbell, 1999; Beresford, 2000; Roberts, 2000; Harper, 2002b.) Mental health service users are, as you will have gathered, already part of the remit of the DRC, so links are being established at policy levels. Abina Parshad-Griffin, in her capacity as Chair of the Mental Health Action Group, refers to what she calls 'mental health disability'.

Is there a *social model* of mental health? Duggan *et al.* suggest this is already accepted, in principle, as part of the National Service Framework, where new skills and new interventions are proposed in order 'to address the root causes of poor mental health, including those which derive from social and environmental deprivation, racism and social roles' (Duggan *et al.*, 2002, p. 12).

The new skills and interventions include consistent relationships with practitioners, working partnerships between users and workers, and access to counselling and talking therapies (Duggan *et al.*, 2002). The implication of developments such as these is the promotion of 'a more holistic understanding of health needs' (Duggan, 2002, p. 3). The final section takes up this challenge.

5 The holistic model of mental health

Interestingly, both the *biopsychosocial approach* and the *social model* of mental health led to the conclusion that what is needed is a more holistic understanding of mental distress. Although we introduce the holistic model here, it is in fact developed more fully in Unit 2 and throughout the rest of the course. This is a model which builds on and enhances the other models, to take a more inclusive view of mental health and distress. It is our preferred way of understanding and approaching mental health because it embraces all aspects of the person, including their genetic make-up as well as their lived experience and their social networks. Figure 1.1 shows the dimensions that make up this all-embracing or holistic view of the person.

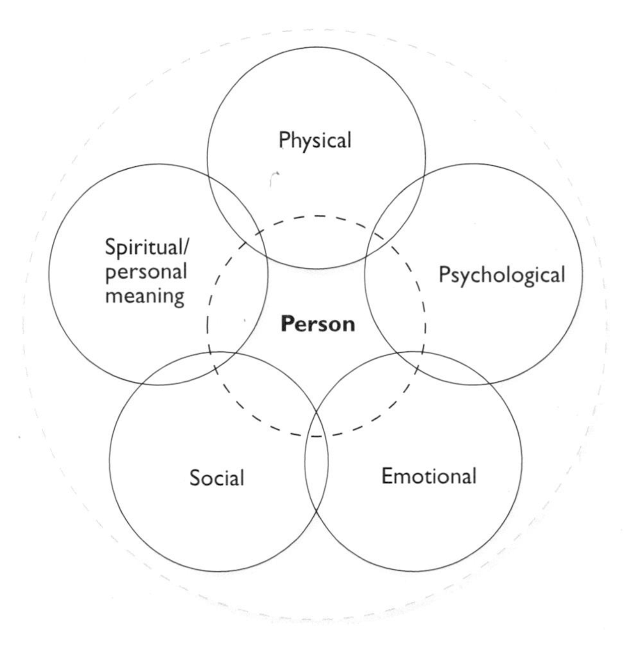

Figure 1.1 The holistic model of mental health (Source: based on Swinton, 2001, p. 36)

The model puts the person at the centre. It incorporates not only the physical and social aspects of the person, but also the psychological, emotional and spiritual dimensions. The outer dotted line symbolises the person's connections with their material and social environment. The links are, of course, two-way: the person interacts with, affects and is affected by environmental factors. This is a model which draws together the best of the medical and social models.

The diagram is one way to think about the holistic model. It is useful because it allows you to 'look inside' the person, to know about the dimensions that you cannot see. Where it is less useful is in showing you the bigger picture of the person – the 'helicopter view', or what happens beyond the dotted line. One way to capture this perspective is to imagine you are in a helicopter watching someone out for a lunchtime run. You see the physical person, and can imagine the psychological, emotional and spiritual uplift they may be getting as they run. But as you go higher, you begin to see the runner's companions from her local group. You also see the university campus where she and her companions are based and, further on, the home she shares with her family. The local group is part of a regional athletics club, which in turn is affiliated to a national body. Some of the runners are training for the London marathon, a national event where athletes from around the world will also be running.

At one level, this is a person out for a lunchtime run. Look harder and you see that the person is involved in a web of connections, stretching from her family and workplace to international events. This is the *holistic view* of a person in their social situation, and it forms the basis of the model we use in the course.

Activity 1.8 **Taking a holistic view**

Learning outcome 5

Take as long as you like for this activity. It is personal to you, so there is no feedback.

You will encounter the holistic model throughout the course. To prepare for this, spend some time now reflecting on the model and how it applies to you. Think about yourself and make notes on each of your five dimensions.

Now take a helicopter view of your life. Put yourself into a bigger picture showing your social ties and connections, and describe it in words or a diagram or picture.

---

6 Conclusion

We ended this unit with the introduction of the holistic model. It is a particularly useful model because it not only represents a way of thinking about and understanding mental distress but also provides an approach to working with and supporting people who are experiencing it. Although the end-point of the unit is a merging of competing perspectives into the holistic model, the journey towards it has involved you in a critical consideration of many familiar and often taken-for-granted ideas about mental distress.

The unit has started the overall course process of *challenging ideas*. So far this has included a review of the social boundaries that divide people and the shortcomings of current explanations of mental distress. As you work your way through the course you may well find that the process of challenging ideas is also a challenge to you personally. This is because it is likely to involve you in reconsidering your existing ideas, values and beliefs. As new ideas come to the fore, the old ones may have to go. Part of the challenge is being open to new ideas and perspectives, and being open to change. Good luck with the rest of the course.

References

Baxter, C., Poonia, K., Ward, L. and Nadirshaw, Z. (1990) *Double Discrimination: Issues and Services for People with Learning Difficulties from Black and Minority Ethnic Communities*, London, King's Fund Centre.

Bentall, R.P. (1992) 'A proposal to classify happiness as a psychiatric disorder', *Journal of Medical Ethics*, Vol. 18, pp. 94–8.

Beresford, P. (2000) 'What have madness and psychiatric system survivors got to do with disability and disability studies?', *Disability and Society*, Vol. 15, No. 1, pp. 167–72.

Beresford, P. and Hopton, J. (2002) 'Our selves and our biology', *Openmind*, Vol. 117, Sept/Oct, pp. 20–1.

Bracken, P. and Thomas, P. (2000) 'Postmodern diagnosis', *Openmind*, Vol. 106, Nov/Dec, p. 19.

Bracken, P. and Thomas, P. (2002) 'Time to move beyond the mind–body split: the mind is not inside but out there in the social world', *British Medical Journal*, Vol. 325, pp. 1433–4.

Campbell, P. (1999) 'The service user/survivor movement' in Newnes, C., Holmes, G. and Dunn, C. (eds) *This is Madness: A Critical Look at Psychiatry and the Future of Mental Health Services*, Ross-on-Wye, PCCS Books, pp. 195–209.

Chadwick, R. (2000) 'Ethical issues in psychiatric care: geneticisation and community care' in Westrin, C.G., Jacobsson, L., Nilstun, T. and Thelander, S. (eds) *Ethics, Law and Human Rights in Psychiatric Care, Acta Psychiatrica Scandinavica Supplementum*, No. 399, Vol. 101, pp. 35–9.

Coppock, V. and Hopton, J. (2000) *Critical Perspectives on Mental Health*, London, Routledge.

Department of Health (1999) *The National Service Framework for Mental Health: Modern Standards and Service Models*, London, DH.

Department of Health (2002) *Draft Mental Health Bill*, Cm 5538-I, London, The Stationery Office.

Dewan, V. (2001) 'Life support' in Read, J. (ed.) *Something Inside So Strong: Strategies for Surviving Mental Distress*, London, Mental Health Foundation, pp. 44–9.

Disability Rights Commission (n.d.) 'A dialogue: "Can mental health service users benefit from disability rights?"' (Transcript of taped conversation between Abina Parshad-Griffin and Liz Sayce), London, DRC.

Disability Rights Commission (2003) 'Coming together – mental health service users and disability rights', www.drc-gb.org/whatwedo/MHAG1.asp [accessed 26/01/04].

Double, D.B. (2002) 'Critical thinking in psychiatry: a positive agenda for change', paper presented to the Mind Annual Conference, Cardiff, November.

Duggan, M. (2002) 'Policy prescriptions', *Community Care*, 14–20 February, pp. 2–3.

Duggan, M. with Cooper, A. and Foster, J. (2002) *Modernising the Social Model in Mental Health: A Discussion Paper*, Social Perspectives Network/TOPSS, England, www.topss.org.uk/uk_eng/news/modsoc_model.pdf [accessed 18/02/04].

Engel, G.L. (1980) 'The clinical application of the biopsychosocial model', *American Journal of Psychiatry*, Vol. 137, pp. 535–44.

Harper, D. (2002a) 'The tyranny of expert language', *Openmind*, Vol. 113, Jan/Feb, pp. 8–9.

Harper, D. (2002b) 'Moving beyond the tyranny of experts', *Openmind*, Vol. 115, May/June, pp. 20–1.

Johnstone, I. (1989) *Users and Abusers of Psychiatry: A Critical Look at Traditional Psychiatric Practice*, London, Routledge.

May, R. (2000) 'Psychosis and recovery', *Openmind*, Vol. 106, Nov/Dec, pp. 24–5.

Oliver, M. and Barnes, C. (1998) *Disabled People and Social Policy: From Exclusion to Inclusion*, London, Longman.

Perkins, R. (2003) 'On the question of genes ...', *Openmind*, Vol. 120, Mar/Apr, p. 6.

Pilgrim, D. (2002) 'The biopsychosocial model in Anglo-American psychiatry: past, present and future', *Journal of Mental Health*, Vol. 11, No. 6, pp. 585–94.

Porter, R. (1999) *The Greatest Gift to Mankind: A Medical History of Humanity from Antiquity to the Present*, London, Fontana.

Roberts, M. (2000) 'Come together? Right now?', *Openmind*, Vol. 106, Nov/Dec, pp. 12–13.

Rose, D. (2002) 'Whose medical model?', *Openmind*, Vol. 113, Jan/Feb, pp. 20–1.

Russo, J. (2001) 'Reclaiming madness' in Read, J. (ed.) *Something Inside so Strong: Strategies for Surviving Mental Distress*, London, Mental Health Foundation, pp. 36–9.

Rutter, M. and Plomin, R. (1997) 'Opportunities for psychiatry from genetic findings', *British Journal of Psychiatry*, Vol. 171, pp. 209–19.

Shaw, I. and Woodward, L. (in press) 'The medicalisation of unhappiness? The management of mental distress in primary care' in Shaw, I. and Kauppinen, K. (eds) *Conceptualising Health and Illness: European Perspectives*, Aldershot, Ashgate, pp. 125–38.

Sibley, D. (1995) *Geographies of Exclusion: Society and Difference in the West*, London, Routledge.

Swinton, J. (2001) *Spirituality and Mental Health Care*, London, Jessica Kingsley.

Unit 2 A Holistic Approach: Hilary's Story

Contents

You will need:

Resources:

Reading 3 'The holistic model'

Your computer

Learning outcomes

After studying this unit you should be able to:

1 discuss how experiences of mental distress may be considered holistically
2 describe the five dimensions of holism
3 apply the holistic model to mental distress
4 explain the implications of developing holistic mental health practices and services.

1 Introduction

What's happening to me? It was the sense of all aspects of home and work life being fractured into a thousand pieces. The real problem was that I was completely unaware of it all until it was too late. Life was passing me by at such a rate I couldn't keep up - I was affected by such a profound sense of tiredness and a total inability to feel in control of anything. Panic, chaos and deep despair combined with a feeling that I was intellectually stupid and, most of all, a fraud. It was a feeling of being trapped and unable to see a way out. Even sleep was hard to come by and I woke at a ridiculously early hour.

I hadn't taken account of all the stress factors that had happened and were continuing to occur. My recent bereavement, my partner's illness and a new job combined to undermine not only my sense of self, but also the confidence that I had anything to offer that would help change the situation.

So began Hilary's account of her experience of depression. Hilary has a full life: she works as a teacher, and in the past has worked as an occupational therapist in mental health. She enjoys gardening and is a part-time student at a local university. You will encounter Hilary throughout this unit and your work on the activities will be of benefit during the course as you become familiar with a holistic approach to mental health and distress through Hilary's story. You learn how her experience of mental distress affected the social, emotional, physical, psychological and spiritual (personal meaning) dimensions of her life. As you work through the course, you will study units that focus on each of these dimensions, but first you turn to holism and the whole person perspective you were introduced to in Unit 1.

2 Holism

You came across the word 'holism' in Unit 1 and were introduced to the holistic model that underpins this course. The course team's model, shown again in Figure 2.1, draws heavily on one developed by Swinton.

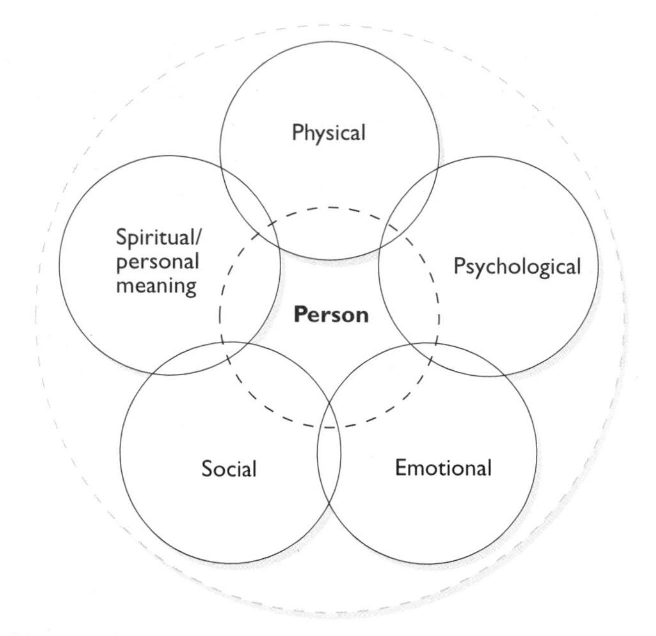

Figure 2.1 The holistic model (Source: based on Swinton, 2001, p. 36)

One way of understanding this model is as a means of bringing together all the dimensions that combine to make us who we are. The important thing to remember is that *all* the dimensions are relevant and make a contribution to our experiences and how we deal with them. In other words, the person at the centre of the model is created by the interplay between the five dimensions. In this unit you go on to explore how Hilary's experiences of depression affected her from a holistic perspective. Some professional approaches focus more on one dimension than on others. For example, medical interventions are directed at the physical dimension, counselling and psychotherapeutic interventions at the psychological dimension. Adopting a holistic approach means that you need to consider influences and interventions for the whole person.

There is also another way of understanding holism: as a means of connecting the whole person, made up of the five dimensions discussed above, to other people. These connections form a never-ending pattern of arrangements that can extend from personal relationships to belonging to a group or culture, sharing a national identity, living in the same environment, living on the same planet and even connections beyond. This approach to holism, represented by the outer dashed line on the holistic model in Figure 2.1, develops an understanding of the whole from the recognition of systems and connections.

Together these two understandings of holism provide a framework which seeks to keep all boundaries of understanding and explanation permeable, so that different dimensions can inform and develop alongside each other. Using these two understandings, holism can help frame dimensions of individual people as well as their wider world.

In the next few sections you examine each of the dimensions of the holistic model through Hilary's experience of depression, before looking in more detail at the principles of holism.

3 The physical dimension

There was no real history of depression in the family, or so I thought. My father did spend some time in the Maudsley [psychiatric hospital], but in those days little was said to me. This fact didn't figure largely in my thinking, as I'd always thought myself a much happier person and wouldn't accept that the past determines the future. But, having said that, I'd used mental health services in the past when I was a newly qualified occupational therapist, following the breakdown of a relationship. I had some counselling and support as well as a course of tricyclics (antidepressants) which I took for two days and couldn't wake up, so stopped. This time was different: extreme tiredness and a sense of wanting to do something but being unable to move very far. I finally even lost my appetite but still ate, almost mechanically, but it was pure comfort food. The prescribed SSRIs (antidepressants) had an almost immediate effect (10 days) but real side effects.

Something stopped the sense of panic and despair. What was most frightening in the physical sense was the excessive ruminations. I hated myself. Still do and always did to an extent, and felt I was unworthy and hopeless at everything. Certainly, without some counselling I fear that it would have been even worse than it now is. Very low self-image and self-esteem. Sleep – waking absolutely on the dot of 3.00 each morning with a sense of panic and terror. Trips to my GP for more pills were so hard. I hated them and what they represented – failure. They were just fine for others, but not me. *But*, along with the sick note, they did tell me that someone thought I wasn't a fraud.

Activity 2.1 **Purely physical?**

15 minutes

Learning outcomes 2 and 3

For this and the following four activities you will need the copy of the holistic model from your Resource File (Reading 3). You will also need five different coloured pencils or pens, one for each activity, or some other way of easily matching your notes to the different dimensions.

You have just read Hilary's view of the physical impact of her mental distress. Now look again at the holistic model.

Write any examples from Hilary's account of the physical aspects of her depression in the physical circle, then note any examples of overlap between the physical and other dimensions and write them in the relevant circle.

Comment

Course testers thought that Hilary's sleep and appetite problems, medication, her family history of mental distress and her lack of energy could all fit in the physical dimension. The stigma surrounding her father's experiences could also fit in the social dimension, and her lack of confidence could fit in the emotional or psychological circles.

Perhaps Hilary's father passed on a gene which contributed to her mental distress. There were changes in her energy level. She described her 'extreme tiredness' and spoke of changes to her appetite and sleep pattern. Medication appears to have played quite a complex role. Antidepressant medication interacts with the body and, as well as the intended effects (Hilary began to feel less depressed), it can have unwanted side effects such as nausea, constipation, weight gain, tremor, blurred vision and sexual problems. Hilary was ambivalent about medication and it played a dual role in her life at that time. On the one hand it represented failure; on the other it gave legitimacy to her situation and experiences – she was not a 'fraud'.

Hilary's account also suggests the relationship between the psychological and the physical dimensions (physical symptoms may have diminished as a result of counselling), and between these and the social dimension. The stigma of mental illness may have made it difficult to talk openly about her father's experience of mental distress, and both symptoms of depression and physical side effects of medication can affect social functioning.

Are physiological responses simply that – physiological? Or do they inevitably link with other dimensions? Genetics increasingly features in discussions about the causes of physical illness and impairment and mental distress. There continues to be much debate about the role of genetics in relation to mental illnesses such as schizophrenia, bipolar disorder and depression. The growing 'genetization of mental illness' poses many ethical challenges, similar to those raised in relation to genetics and physical disability (Dowson, 2003). For example, genetic technologies have linked conditions such as Down's syndrome with 'rogue' configurations of genes (Drake, 1999). This, Drake argues, leads to value judgements about 'the causes of disability, the status of disabled people, the quality of their lives and the amount of support provided by society to parents and disabled people' (p. 135).

If the public welcome the use of knowledge about genetic technologies in, for example, providing information to prospective parents about whether to have a pregnancy terminated, Dowson (2003) asks what that says about society's attitudes to disabled people. It seems unlikely that depression is caused by a gene. A holistic view is that there are several causes, including environmental, psychological and biological factors (Brown, 1996).

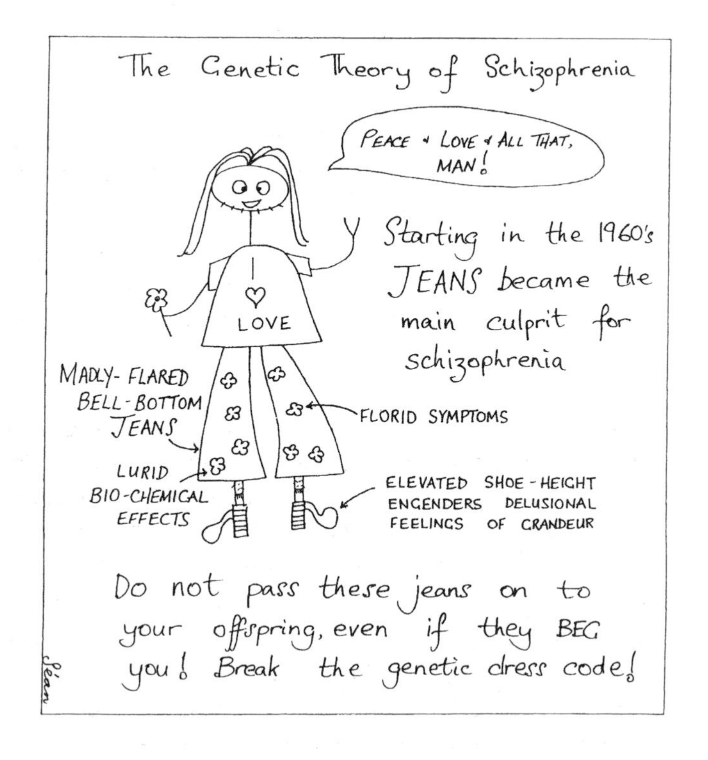

In response to the question 'Is depression inherited?' the Mental Health Foundation suggests:

> There is some evidence that depression seems to run in families, but there is no single gene which causes depression. A family history of depression may increase the risk, but this may be because of difficulties the person has in coping, and it certainly does not mean that depression is inevitable.
>
> (Mental Health Foundation, 2000, p. 8)

In the Introduction and Study Guide and Unit 1 you met Rachel Perkins, a clinical psychologist who has a diagnosis of manic depression. Perkins thinks her mental health problems are caused by the way chemicals in her brain called neurotransmitters work, and are part of her genetic inheritance. However, she doesn't think this is the whole story:

> Even if my manic depression is associated with the action of a single gene, or the interaction of a number of genes, this is not the whole story. [...] The consequences of manic depression for your life and opportunities are heavily influenced by the social and physical environment – by things that happen. The fact that I had a stable upbringing, good education, lots of people to value and encourage me, has greatly contributed to the way I have been able to use my genetic inheritance.

She goes on to say:

> I resent the implication that, had my genetic endowment been discovered early enough, I could have been aborted, or not conceived in the first place. This implies that my life is not worth living, that I have nothing to contribute. The disability and much of the distress associated with madness are not an inevitable result of genetic endowment but a consequence of the prejudice and discrimination that mean people are excluded from social and economic life.
>
> To be sure, I detest my depressions [...] but I would contend that the peculiarities of brain chemistry are also responsible for a great part of the positive energy and creativity in my life.
>
> (Perkins, 2003, p. 6)

What about other physical dimensions of depression? An extreme view called 'reductionism' is that all psychological experiences can be 'reduced' to the activities of the brain. Toates (2002) cites Crick as saying:

> that 'You', your joys and your sorrows, your memories and your ambitions, your sense of personal identity and free will, are in fact no more than the behaviour of a vast assembly of nerve cells and their associated molecules.
>
> (Toates, 2002, p. 228)

Although the view outlined by Crick is quite extreme, it is known that depression is linked with changes in the activity of particular brain chemicals, the neurotransmitters that Rachel Perkins mentioned, which affect mood and thinking. However, these chemicals, for example serotonin, are also affected by factors such as activity and exercise (Mental Health Foundation, 2000).

So, back to Hilary. The focus in this section is on the physical dimension of her experience – the possibility of genetic inheritance, the physical symptoms she experienced and the antidepressant medication she was prescribed. In the next section, you read Hilary's description of the effects of depression on the psychological dimension of her experiences.

4 The psychological dimension

Not being able to really express all the feelings, mixed with a kind of anger and sense of being wronged. Wanting to cry, but apart from the first few days no tears. When they did come they were almost separate from the feelings that went with them. A deep unhappiness and even deeper sadness, mostly about work and the total inability to perform and the lack of belief that things could get better. In fact they couldn't, not until the depression had lifted a bit and I could see the feelings were better than they were at the point when I had to give up and see the GP. The GP was the person who could validate what I was feeling, but equally I thought she would find me a fraud and send me back to work. The very worst thing of all for me was that I couldn't concentrate or read, and I didn't understand anything I read. Things that I had taught for 15 years were now a complete mystery, and it was truly terrifying.

Along with that I had the most appalling memory, especially for names and faces, and I seriously wondered whether I was in the early stages of dementia. I realised, or was forced to realise, that along with a job that was new and difficult, I was depressed. I looked for instant cures and relief. I hoped the next task would be better than the last and I would turn the magic corner. No relief came and I suddenly did realise, as a teacher and a professional, that depression, or whatever it was, hits the thing you need the most. I couldn't think, write or perform any type of analysis at all. I could no longer learn, heard no positive messages and became ever more fixed that I was a victim and there was no way out of it. I was going to lose my job and we would lose our home. This all added to the intellectual pressure on a brain that felt like mush.

Hilary's account of the psychological (which she calls 'intellectual') effects of depression is powerful. The psychological dimension includes cognition – in other words, the way she thought about her situation as well as how she could learn and remember.

Activity 2.2 **Pursuing the psychological**

15 minutes — Learning outcomes 2 and 3

In this activity you will add to the model you began in Activity 2.1.

Using a different colour, write any examples from Hilary's story of the psychological impacts of depression in the psychological circle. Then note any examples that you consider overlap between the psychological and other dimensions and write them in the relevant circles.

Comment

A loss of ability to work, to remember and to concentrate and an inability to express feelings were some of the factors course testers identified as fitting in the psychological dimension. However, they also noted that other dimensions are affected. For example, the social dimension is affected by Hilary's inability to work, and the emotional dimension is affected by her perception of failure.

This element of the holistic model, the psychological dimension, covers everyday experiences and relates to memory, learning and understanding. The fact that her depression compromised Hilary's ability to function intellectually was all the more devastating for her work as a teacher and a mature student. However, she also writes of a 'deeper sadness', of her 'unhappiness' and an inability to cry, which suggest the significance of the emotional dimension.

Cognition – the way people understand and think about their situation – places the ability to use the mind effectively, to understand and to reason, at centre stage. It has been suggested that this is valued more or less highly according to the circumstances and context. Early philosophers suggested that it is these qualities of intellect and reasoning that determine whether you are a person or not! In 1690 the British philosopher John Locke, for example, wrote:

> we must consider what *person* stands for; – which, I think, is a thinking intelligent being, that has reason and reflection, and can consider itself as itself, the same thinking thing, in different times and places;
>
> (Locke, 1974, p. 67)

Locke defines a person in terms of the ability to think, to reflect and to be self-conscious. Are people 'persons' regardless of their ability to think and reflect? What Locke highlights is the high value placed on reason and intellectual functioning. This has implications for people experiencing mental distress if their capacity to make decisions about themselves and their lives is called into question.

5 The emotional dimension

As I write I'm aware of feelings that make me deeply sad, almost fighting back the tears that I couldn't really express at the time. Now they are painful tears. Last time I must have bored everyone with them, but they weren't at the level of my soul. Looking back on it, I'd just had a holiday at a place with happy and sad memories, and realised that most of it just passed me by in a vague time of withdrawal and weariness. It was as if the sun shone across the bay but not on our side at all. Even going out for a walk on my beloved island hills did nothing. At the time I felt nothing at all. I was too much of a coward to think about death, but I guess it must have been there, because I was always somehow pleased when somebody was with me even though half of me didn't want them there.

This may be the dimension many people think of first when the word depression is mentioned. Depression is, after all, described as a 'disorder' of mood and mood is very much connected with the emotions. Hilary writes about the emotions she experiences as she writes and about how she had difficulty expressing these emotions at the time of her depression. But what are the emotions? And, again, how might this dimension connect with others?

Activity 2.3 **The place of emotions**

15 minutes

Learning outcomes 2 and 3

Return again to the model you have been developing in the last two activities. Using another colour, write down any examples from Hilary's story that fit in the emotional dimension circle, then note any examples that you consider overlap between the emotional and other dimensions in the relevant circle.

Comment

One course tester commented:

> The effects of the emotional impact of depression spanned all of the five dimensions. Sadness, withdrawal, loss and weariness were the key impacts in the emotional dimension, but there was also sadness and weariness at a deeper level which linked with the personal meaning dimension, and also fitted into the physical dimension. Hilary was not sure she wanted people with her and worried that she'd bored them with her crying – fitting both the psychological and social dimensions.

Discussing the emotional impact of communicating and relating in health and social care, Rogers (Open University, 2004) notes the distinction between feelings and emotions. Feelings are described as neutral, neither good nor bad: as energetic responses to internal and external environments which 'alert us to take action in some way'. Rogers identifies five basic emotions – anger, sadness, fear, happiness, disgust – which play a significant part in how people are in relation to themselves and others. But are these emotions neutral?

In a study conducted in Sweden, Hedelin and Strandmark (2001) explored the meaning of depression for older women and the strength of emotions the women experienced. Women spoke of alienation and fear; of meaninglessness, emptiness and hopelessness; and of self-searching and guilt. One woman spoke of the boundaries which seemed to exist between herself and the rest of the world:

> You live in another world. You become isolated from real life ... there is a wall in between. Everything becomes diffuse and unreal and strange. You sit and look at people – how do they have the strength, the strength to laugh, the strength to read? You are ... you are so empty and so afraid and think yourself so strange ... you just can't function in a normal way but perhaps nobody else notices. You just sit there and say 'yes' and 'is that so?' and try to act as usual and not show how horrid everything is.
>
> (Hedelin and Strandmark, 2001, pp. 409–10)

So far the focus of the dimensions has been very much on Hilary as an individual – on the physical, psychological and emotional dimensions of her experience. Next, you consider the social dimension.

6 The social dimension

I hated meeting people and had to be forced out of the house, by myself. I went to work one day in the car and stayed 20 minutes and had to come back. The house was safe. Even my garden was a place where too much energy was needed. In any case, none of the vegetables would grow for me, would they? The fact they did was down to luck and certainly not any gardening skill I might have. There was a strange sense of childlike dependence yet at the same time an awful feeling of being trapped by my partner of 13 years. I was a child, I just wanted to be alone. But being alone was frightening. The telephone was a constant source of dread and terror to me. I dreaded that like no other. Yet alone in the house I felt hopeful that it might ring and someone would say it's all right, everything is fine. The trip to the health centre to see the counsellor was the social highlight, but was mixed with dread because so much tumbled out that I had kept under close control, and certainly did not speak of with others.

I only wanted two or three people near me most of the time. I must have worn out others who rang and had me telling the same story repeatedly, and usually ending in floods of tears as well. The world, which I cared about so much as a feminist, was now alien to me. I didn't want to know anything, about birds, wildlife, or even go out and see the countryside that surrounds me.

My partner set me small targets like making a phone call or putting the washing out, that's how bad it had become. At the time I couldn't see it and only now realise that given a chance I would have just sat all day in one place thinking about how hopeless it all was, so I might as well be on my own. The friends who stuck with me through it all are even more precious now.

The social dimension considers people in relation to other people – in one-to-one relationships; in families; at work; relaxing and socialising. As well as being an inclusive concept, 'social' may also exclude. If work is part of the social dimension, what of people who do not work for whatever reason? Hilary continued to be able to communicate her feelings and experiences, but for some people communication itself may be difficult. Social exclusion may be very real for someone experiencing depression – not just during a period of distress but as a result of the stigma attached to a label of mental illness. In Unit 6 you will look in more detail at stigma, social exclusion and citizenship.

Activity 2.4 **Choosing to be social?**

15 minutes Learning outcomes 2 and 3

You have now read Hilary's account of the social impact of her experiences of depression. Your holistic model is likely to be looking fairly full by now, and this activity will add yet more information and colour. Write any examples from Hilary's story that fit in the social dimension circle, and note any examples which you consider overlap between the social dimension and other dimensions.

Comment The impact on Hilary's identity was noted by several course testers – her identities as a professional, partner, friend, feminist and gardener were all affected by the depression. These identities were not confined to the social dimension, but spread across all aspects of her life.

Among other things, Hilary's account highlights the important role that relationships can play in people's lives, alongside the ambivalent attitudes that someone experiencing mental distress can have towards other people. As well as relative economic security, Hilary had a supportive relationship with her partner. However, not all relationships are supportive. Some may be the reverse and may add to feelings of isolation and distress. On the other hand, living with someone who is depressed may be very challenging for a partner or relative. Hilary also wrote of her loneliness. Loneliness may take many forms and people differ in their perceptions of what it involves. Being alone is not the same as being lonely. You may value the time you have alone, for example to get on with your course work!

The fifth and final dimension is that of spirituality, probably the most challenging and elusive in terms of definition.

7 The spiritual or personal meaning dimension

It was after two or three weeks of being off work that I began a kind of spiritual 'journey', one that I am still travelling very slowly. I began to be more meditative, but even to this day I find concentrating very hard and it all feels a bit superficial. My old beliefs just made me cry more, and the sense of sadness still comes over me when I realise what was happening, and still is. I am angry that this has been taken from me, and long for time to rebuild it. At the time there was no hope in my life. I felt so disconnected from everything. Looking outside of myself was too physically and mentally hard. I doubted my purpose in our relationship, doubted my own ability to change my life and felt I had lost a purpose in my existence. Life was just a series of actions that needed to be completed.

However, my love of music is gradually coming back, and how I had missed that. It was, along with work, the thing that kept me trundling on. I was afraid to listen to music because it awoke a longing that made me tearful, too much to bear. All the guilt from leaving the Christian upbringing also added to the burden. All the censored voices of right-wing fundamentalism in which I had been raised began to surface anew. Those are the voices that in my present, more healed state I work on with my counsellor, a wonderful Jewish man who challenges all the time, but always has some words of wisdom. Counselling is not my new religion, but it certainly helps to have someone who expects nothing, knows me and sees clearly through my ramblings.

Activity 2.5 **Meaning and spirituality**

15 minutes

Learning outcomes 2 and 3

You have now read Hilary's account of the final dimension in the model, the spiritual dimension, and are moving towards a picture of the 'whole' Hilary. Using the last of your colours, write any examples from Hilary's story that fit in the spiritual dimension circle and note any examples that you think overlap between the spiritual dimension and other dimensions.

Comment

Hilary's description of meaning and spirituality and her experience of depression have a number of threads. She writes of making a 'spiritual journey'; of being 'meditative'; of feelings of hopelessness; of doubting purpose in her relationship; of dealing with her rejection of her Christian upbringing; and of her Jewish counsellor. She points out that 'counselling is not my new religion'.

One view of spirituality (which is related to nursing) is that it is:

> a unifying force of a person; the essence of being that permeates all of life and is manifested in one's being, knowing, and doing; the interconnectedness with self, others, nature, and God/Life Force/Absolute/Transcendent.
>
> (Dossey and Guzzetta, 2000, p. 7)

And another:

> the essence of our being, which permeates our living and infuses our unfolding awareness of who and what we are, our purpose in being, and our inner resources; and shapes our life journey [...] The term *spirituality* derives from the Latin *spiritus*, meaning breath, and relates to the Greek *pneuma* or breath, which refers to the vital spirit or soul. Spirituality is the essence of who we are and how we are in the world and, like breathing, is essential to our human existence.
>
> (Burkhardt and Jacobson, 2000, pp. 91–2)

Meaning and spirituality are inextricably linked, but spirituality is not necessarily linked to religion. The meaning you give to events, experiences and emotions will be affected to a greater or lesser extent by what you believe. This is a challenging topic to which you will return later in the course, in Unit 18.

Spirituality and meaning are the final dimension in the holistic model you have been looking at in this unit. But have these added up to a holistic picture of Hilary?

8 Holism revisited

Up to now you have concentrated on the five elements of the holistic model as they relate to Hilary. In this section you focus more on the theoretical basis for holism and its practice implications. You may have read about holism in relation to complementary or alternative therapies. If you have experience of social or health care work you may have heard people speak about a holistic approach or holistic medicine or health care. Is this interest in holism new? One view is that holism is a reaction to medical approaches. There is, however, some evidence that holistic models were present in Western medicine in the first half of the 20th century (Lawrence and Weisz, 1998), and they are integral to approaches to health in other cultures. So you could see holism as a reincarnation of what was there prior to modern medical specialisms, although it did not have a name as such. In the UK some medical practitioners have sought to promote holistic interventions with the establishment of the British Holistic Medical Association (BHMA) in 1983. The Association has the mission:

> to educate doctors, medical students, allied health professionals and members of the general public in the principles and practice of holistic medicine.
>
> (BHMA, 2003)

This suggests that a holistic approach is compatible with at least some aspects of medicine. The BHMA has a broad interest in health and is not specifically focused on mental health. Indeed, a holistic approach suggests that all aspects of wellbeing are interconnected. The BHMA gives a definition of holism and suggests how it may be put into practice. So, having considered what Hilary understands by holism, what does it mean to mental health practice and services?

Activity 2.6 **Holism and health**

30 minutes

Learning outcomes 1 and 4

Up to now you've looked at holism in relation to individual people. How does it apply to a service or to mental health practice? Go to the K272 course website. Using ROUTES, go to the BHMA website and click on the link 'What is holistic medicine'. You may want to print out the page. Now make some notes on how holistic a mental health service or project you are familiar with appears to be, using the BHMA principles as a guideline.

Comment One course tester wrote:

> This response is based on my experience working in a medium secure mental health unit. The primary focus of the service is psychiatric responses to offending behaviour and related mental distress. It operates in a clear legal and public protection framework. Individuals are pathologised and cut off from their social worlds – they are not interconnected. Complementary practitioners are only available to women patients (who receive a more sympathetic approach). Those therapists have little input into clinical decisions and much is 'done for' people; self-help is limited.

What might holistic interventions look like? They are likely to be diverse, whether they are practices or services. For example, holistic practices might include the partner of someone experiencing depression being directed to a relatives' support group (social and emotional dimensions), while the person concerned is offered occupational therapy (physical and psychological dimensions) as well as medication (physical dimension). A holistic service might include a drop-in centre that changes its activities and hours during Ramadan so that members can still make use of the support available (the social and spiritual/personal meaning dimensions). What is common to holistic interventions is that the focus is not solely the separate elements of distress or illness.

Holism has been described as a 'big view' which takes account of the inner and outer environment of the person (Brom, 1995). The two ways of understanding holism you have already encountered in this unit are similar to what Brom describes as inner, physical and emotional worlds and outer, social and interpersonal worlds. From these understandings comes the view that the whole is greater than the sum of its parts. Seedhouse (2000, pp. 59–60) suggests that holism makes two main claims: that a whole cannot be fully understood even if all its parts are understood separately, and that the separate parts cannot be fully understood apart from the whole. What does he mean by these statements? Take the first:

> A whole cannot be fully understood even if all its parts are understood separately.

Seedhouse uses the nuclear family as an example of this statement. A family may comprise many parts – mother, father, daughter, and so on. All of them have individual bodies, lives and histories. However, there will also be a shared family history, shaped and created by the individuals in the family and their interactions with each other and wider society. The family develops its own history, ways of understanding and ways of doing things that are particular to them. So, Seedhouse argues, even if you know all the family members individually, that is not enough to fully understand the family as a whole.

He gives another example of this by presenting a detailed description of the physiological dimensions of the processes involved in smelling a rose. He argues that:

> though correct on its own terms, this description fails to capture the importance of the experience of smelling a gorgeous rose on a sublime summer's evening.
>
> (Seedhouse, 2000, p. 60)

There are many examples of 'wholes' and 'parts'. A 'whole' might be an organisation (such as the National Health Service, a voluntary organisation such as Mind or a community association, or a factory), a person (such as you) or an organ of the body (your brain, for example). The parts of organisations such as the NHS or Mind might include specific services, people who provide and receive services, management structures and so on. 'Person parts' could be organs, tissues and cells. However, knowing about cell and blood structure does not provide a holistic understanding of the person: knowledge about the parts does not mean knowledge about the whole.

Now, Seedhouse's second statement:

> The separate parts of something cannot be fully understood apart from the whole.

Returning to the example of the family, this statement suggests that a family member cannot be understood adequately separate from their family. You need to understand a family before you can understand any of its members. But is it the case that aspects of organs, people or institutions cannot be understood apart from the whole? The relationship between 'parts' and 'wholes' is challenging. However, it seems possible to understand a good deal without necessarily knowing everything about the whole. It is also questionable whether anyone is ever in a position to fully understand any 'part', particularly where people are involved, although this is not to say that they should not try to understand the parts of the whole and the whole itself.

The boundaries between dimensions within the person, in other words intrapersonal boundaries, are not solid or static. The boundaries between the dimensions of the holistic model in Figure 2.1 are permeable, continuously shifted by the complexity of individual experiences. Emotions can impact on the physical, the physical on the social; and meaning has the potential to impact on all the other dimensions. Hilary's story illustrates the permeability of boundaries.

Up to now you have encountered two understandings of holism that help frame dimensions of the person as well as the wider world and have looked at the challenging relationships between parts and wholes.

What are the principles underlying holism? Brom (1995), although focusing on medicine and not referring specifically to mental health and wellbeing, has suggested that several principles underpin holistic understandings, including:

> - Each individual is recognised as an integrated system. Removing any part out of that system requires a readjustment of the whole system. [...]
> - The human system is an open system. It is in contact outwardly with the surrounding environment and inwardly with 'spiritual' dimensions. [...]
> - The human system is not only biochemical but is a multidimensional system. [...]
> - There are multiple causes to disease and no single cause can ever be isolated.
>
> (Brom, 1995, p. 15)

Now you consider each of these principles in relation to the holistic model used in this course.

Each individual is recognised as an integrated system. Removing any part out of that system requires a readjustment of the whole system.

The five dimensions of the person are interrelated and so when one is changed or altered in some way there will be impacts on the other dimensions. These interrelated changes can be seen in both the cause of distress and potential responses to it. So, if someone becomes unemployed (social dimension) they will have a loss of income and may not be able to maintain a healthy diet (physical dimension); they may also experience low self-esteem (psychological dimension) and begin to wonder what their life is about (meaning dimension). An intervention which focused on one dimension would only be partially helpful.

Staying with the same example, it may be possible to develop self-esteem by taking advantage of psychological therapies. However, raised self-esteem would not necessarily provide increased income or employment or help to find meaning in life. In the same way, finding meaning or spiritual comfort will not necessarily help someone to have a healthy diet. On the other hand, because all the dimensions are interconnected there will be changes to them all, albeit small, as a result of a bigger change in one dimension. Therefore increased self-esteem may mean having more belief in oneself and so making more job applications.

The human system is an open system. It is in contact outwardly with the surrounding environment and inwardly with 'spiritual' dimensions.

It is important, then, to think from the inside outwards, as well as from the outside inwards, when adopting a holistic approach. This involves using both understandings of holism you encountered in Section 2, where all dimensions of the whole person are considered alongside the wider system or world. Brom focuses here on the boundary between the spiritual and the environmental worlds or, as he puts it, the inner and outer worlds. Some people don't see a necessary distinction between the two. For example, Suman Fernando, a psychiatrist interviewed for the course, says:

> I think there's the general spirituality where it's a connection between people, the cosmos, an ecological approach to life ... interaction and a sort of unity. The unity of people with one another, essentially, that is spirituality.

Spirituality is a complex concept and is much broader than religion or faith. Fernando talks here about connections and unity and the wider dimensions of holism. In Unit 18 you will consider the interconnections between inner and outer worlds and meaning and spirituality in the world of mental health.

The human system is not only biochemical but is a multidimensional system.

There are narrow, biochemical and broad, multidimensional views of health. One view, usually labelled a narrow or 'negative' view, is that health is the absence of illness or disorder. In this view the presence of symptoms of illness mean that health is absent. On first glance this seems an obvious statement. However, it may not be as simple as that. Take Peter, who has been given a diagnosis of bipolar disorder (also known as manic depression). On the one hand you might argue that he has a major mental illness and so could not be considered to be 'healthy'. However, he has developed ways of dealing with his experiences and is currently neither depressed nor elated. So at this particular point in time it could be argued that he is healthy.

A broad, multidimensional view of health, and the one used by the World Health Organization, is that 'Health is a state of complete physical, mental and social well-being and not merely the absence of disease or infirmity' (WHO, 1946). The first view may be criticised for being very narrow and the second for being overly broad and idealistic. Perhaps a more helpful way of viewing health and illness is to see them as two ends of a continuum that changes over time. So, for example, in relation to his overall mental health Peter could be located at the illness and distress end of the continuum because of his diagnosis of bipolar disorder. However, he could just as easily be located at the health and wellbeing end because he is not distressed at this particular time.

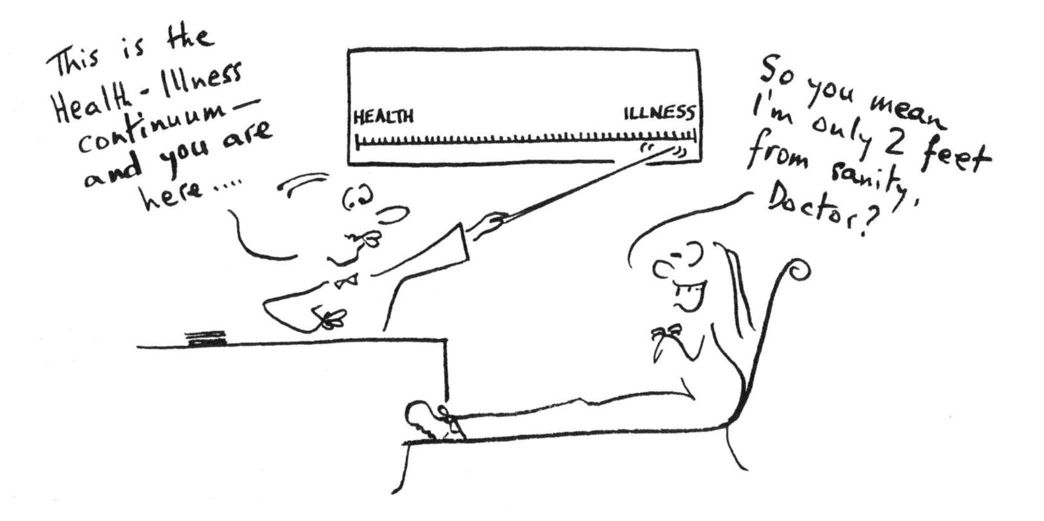

In a similar way, Reeta has not had any contact with mental health services and rarely visits her GP, so she could be located at the health end of the continuum. However, she is experiencing a great deal of stress at the moment as a result of changes at work, and the physical effects of the stress are causing her some difficulties. So she could also be placed at the illness end of the continuum. Stress is a particularly useful example of the interconnections between dimensions of a person, and you will look at stress again in Unit 5.

There are multiple causes to disease and no single cause can ever be isolated.

If you have experienced mental distress or know someone who has, it is likely that you will have wondered why: 'Why me/her/him?' and 'Why now?' There is no agreement about what precipitates or causes periods of mental distress. Some people favour biological explanations (it's all in the body, brain, genes); others favour sociological explanations (it's to do with poverty, family, work, the environment); still others prefer psychological explanations (it's to do with personality, character, adjustment). Some people favour a combination of them all. Toates, for example, writes of depression:

> Is depression biological or social? Such a dichotomy is unhelpful since it divides the world in a way that is not logical. Changes in synapses affect the way that we interpret events in the world. Conversely, events in the world, such as exposure to trauma, inevitably have consequences in the nervous system. Therefore, depression is bound to be both biological *and* social.
>
> (Toates, 2002, p. 276)

So far in this unit you have read Hilary's story, encountered the BHMA's definition of holism and read what Seedhouse and Brom suggest are important dimensions of holism. But what are the practical implications of holism?

Activity 2.7 **Holism and you**

Allow 30 minutes

Learning outcome 1

Now spend some time thinking about what holism means to you. Write down your ideas and try to illustrate your explanation by including an example of what a holistic mental health service or practice might be like for a service user/survivor.

Comment

Course testers identified several dimensions of holism. One noted:

> Holism recognises that different people respond differently to different methods of support. Equally, it acknowledges that people may respond better to different methods at different stages of their lives.

Another wrote:

> In terms of mental health, the application of a holistic approach would bring into consideration the many and varied dimensions of someone's life and context. Holism would broaden the options available to include, for example, reiki and Indian head massage as well as chemical preparations.

Holistic approaches seem a long way from the help some people have had from mental health services and practitioners. Writing in *Openmind* about his experiences of depression, Nick Taussig notes he was confused by the different interventions that practitioners offered. He questions why different mental health 'methodologies and practices' have never been integrated:

> The recovery from these collapses or breakdowns has always been slow and painful. And each one has brought a different treatment, ranging from psychopharmacology, to cognitive behavioural therapy, to psychoanalysis. [...] On each occasion when I called on them and their providers to help me out of the dark, each of them stood proudly alone, protesting their own therapeutic power and efficacy, almost like rival politicians at the ballot box before polling day.
>
> (Taussig, 2002, p. 10)

The rivalry between explanations was not helpful at all for Taussig: what mattered most to him was that he felt well. It seems as though he was caught between different explanations and interventions, with no one taking a holistic perspective.

There are many challenges involved in developing a holistic perspective, for people who work in mental health services as well as for people who use the services. For example, people may have particular expectations of psychiatrists, social workers and nurses when they come into contact with their particular services. They may not want professionals to ask about – or indeed, know about – other areas of their lives.

9 Conclusion

You have considered the relationship between 'parts' and 'wholes' and explored each of the five dimensions of holism as they were experienced by Hilary. Each dimension is a fundamental part of the whole individual, while at the same time connected with other parts. Holism is the view that the whole is more important than the sum of its parts. Hilary is then more important than her five dimensions. We could extend the parts further to include dimensions not yet discussed – sexuality, for example. Which dimension would it fit into? And what about the 'whole'? You might also have thought about Hilary's different identities: as woman, teacher, student, partner, service user/survivor and gardener.

Hedelin and Strandmark note the multidimensional and unique experience of depression:

> The women described depression as a severe suffering affecting their relation to and trust in themselves, in other people, and in the opportunities offered by life. The depression, thus, included the woman's whole life space. The depression was described as multidimensional, where mental, physical, social and existential subaspects interacted, and previous experiences merged with the current situation. [...] there is no definitive, comprehensive, and overriding description, set of criteria, or model of depression; there are an infinite number of possibilities of experiencing depression.
>
> (Hedelin and Strandmark, 2001, pp. 413, 414)

When people experience mental distress, it may result in a change in their view of their identity. An additional identity may have been shaped – that of service user/survivor. In Unit 1 you were introduced to a range of terms used to describe people who have had experiences of mental distress. Each of them carries particular meanings and images. It is not inevitable that people who use mental health services will embrace the identity of service user/survivor. But many people who use them find they have little choice but to be defined by their experience. For example, people who have had no contact with mental health services for many years may find the identity clings to them when applying for a job or seeking insurance.

A service user/survivor identity may bring some benefits: access to services and treatments (but not necessarily those the person prefers), welfare benefits and some protection under the Disability Discrimination Act. But these 'benefits' come with a package of negative attitudes which may be reinforced by discrimination and harassment in areas such as employment, relationships, financial services and legal justice. Such an identity may also obscure other identities people have, and can often be seen as the key defining feature of someone who is in contact with mental health services, even though people see themselves in many different ways and have many identities in their lives. You have already seen Hilary's identities of woman, teacher, student, partner and gardener. Along with everyone else who uses mental health services, she is much more than a service user/survivor.

For many people depression is a devastating experience which affects their whole person. Hilary's account of the impact of her depression has illustrated the lived reality of the five dimensions and their interrelationships. Hilary is unique and her experience of depression is unique. In a paper about the relationship between the arts and medicine, Scott notes:

> each person is like every other person, like some other people, like no other person. Each of us contains within us both general patterns and the particular, that which is peculiar to me and my context.
>
> (Scott, 2000, p. 5)

Hilary's experience is not something that can be reduced to individual parts. Nor can it be neatly transferred to other people who are experiencing depression. However, it illustrates the importance of a holistic approach in capturing the complexity and richness of experience.

References

British Holistic Medical Association (2003) 'Welcome to the website of the British Holistic Medical Association', www.bhma.org [accessed 23/03/04].

Brom, B. (1995) 'Holism: definition and principles', *International Journal of Alternative and Complementary Medicine*, April, pp. 14–17.

Brown, G. (1996) 'Genetics of depression: a social science perspective', *International Review of Psychiatry*, Vol. 8, No. 4, pp. 387–402.

Burkhardt, M. and Jacobson, M. (2000) 'Spirituality and health' in Dossey, B.M., Keegan, L. and Guzzetta, C.E. (eds) *Holistic Nursing: A Handbook for Practice* 3rd edition, Gaithersburg, Md., Aspen Publishers.

Dossey, B.M. and Guzzetta, C.E. (2000) 'Holistic nursing practices' in Dossey, B.M., Keegan, L. and Guzzetta, C.E. (eds) *Holistic Nursing: A Handbook for Practice*, 3rd edition, Gaithersburg, Md., Aspen Publishers.

Dowson, S. (2003) 'Whose life is it anyway?', *Community Care*, 24–30 July, pp. 38–9.

Drake, R. (1999) *Understanding Disability Politics*, Basingstoke, Macmillan.

Hedelin, B. and Strandmark, M. (2001) 'The meaning of depression from the life-world perspective of elderly women', *Issues in Mental Health Nursing*, Vol. 22, pp. 401–20.

Lawrence, C. and Weisz, G. (eds) (1998) *Greater than the Parts: Holism in Biomedicine 1920–1950*, Oxford, Oxford University Press.

Locke, J. (1974) 'An essay concerning human understanding' (first published 1690), *The Empiricists*, New York, Anchor Press/Doubleday.

Mental Health Foundation (2000) *All About Depression*, London, Mental Health Foundation. Available from: www.mentalhealth.org.uk/html/content/all_about_depression.pdf [accessed 15/03/04].

Open University (2004) K205 *Communication and Relationships in Health and Social Care*, Block 3 *The Person in the Process*, Unit 11 'The emotional impact of communicating and relating in health and social care', Milton Keynes, The Open University.

Perkins, R. (2003) 'On the question of genes ...', *Openmind*, Vol. 120, Mar/Apr, p. 6.

Scott, P.A. (2000) 'The relationship between the arts and medicine', *Journal of Medical Ethics: Medical Humanities*, Vol. 26, pp. 3–8.

Seedhouse, D. (2000) *Practical Nursing Philosophy: The Universal Ethical Code*, Chichester, Wiley.

Swinton, J. (2001) *Spirituality and Mental Health Care*, London, Jessica Kingsley.

Taussig, N. (2002) 'My cure is better than yours', *Openmind*, Vol. 117, Sept/Oct, p. 10.

Toates, F. (2002) 'Biological processes and psychological explanation', Chapter 4 in Miell, D., Phoenix, A. and Thomas, K. (eds) (2002) *Mapping Psychology 1* (DSE212 *Exploring Psychology*, Book 1, Part 1), Milton Keynes, The Open University, pp. 223–81.

World Health Organization (1946) *Constitution of the World Health Organization*, whqlibdoc.who.int/hist/official_records/constitution.pdf [accessed 23/03/04].

Unit 3 Relationship Boundaries

Contents

You will need:

Resources:

Reading 4 'Formal observations and engagement'

Audio 1 'Shifting boundaries'

Learning outcomes

After studying this unit you should be able to:

1 understand the significance of roles and relationships in relation to mental health and distress
2 explore the place of boundaries in relationships
3 discuss the significance of power in relationships between mental health workers and service users
4 reflect on challenges and possibilities which arise when workers become service users
5 consider the regulation of relationships in the context of mental health.

1 Introduction

In Unit 2 you focused on the five dimensions of a holistic model and how they interact in relation to Hilary's experience of mental distress. You primarily explored the understanding of holism as a means of bringing together the five dimensions that combine to make us who we are. You now move towards the second understanding set out in that unit: holism as a means of connecting the whole person, made up of those five dimensions, to other people.

A study by the Mental Health Foundation (Faulkner and Layzell, 2000) asked service users/survivors to identify coping strategies that were helpful during periods of mental distress. Many people highlighted relationships as having a key role. When people were asked what was helpful in the relationships they engaged in, a number of aspects were mentioned: not being alone; being trusted, believed and understood; sharing experiences; support and encouragement. The respondents also pointed to practical elements of relationships which were beneficial, such as the advocacy, help and information offered.

On a day-to-day basis you may engage in a wide range of relationships. Some of these may be with family members, some with work colleagues, fellow students, friends or neighbours, and some may be with people who provide social and health care services. These relationships will vary a great deal. You may have certain expectations of different relationships, the roles people have in them and the relative importance and significance of each. People view particular relationships in different ways. Some people, for example, see friends regularly and family rarely; for others the opposite is the case. However, regardless of the way you view particular relationships, in general they are of the utmost importance – for better and sometimes for worse – in terms of your development and your sense of self.

In this unit you focus on the challenges involved in maintaining and breaking boundaries: in continuous observation, where a worker constantly observes a patient; in situations where workers need to maintain appropriate boundaries; when changing roles from worker to service user and back again (and the opportunities this presents); and in re-evaluating friendships in situations where people need to consider the nature of the relationship (and values which may take priority over friendship).

2 The challenges and significance of relationships

The relationships people form are influenced by the social systems in which they live, and the boundaries within them are socially constructed (Tronto, 1993, p. 11). Take, for example, relationships with neighbours. If you live in a terraced house with windows looking straight on to the street, you are likely to see neighbours regularly and may get to know some of them quite well. If you live in a large block of flats (or, for that matter, a detached house) it is possible that you see your neighbours only rarely. If you live in shared accommodation you may have little choice about whether you have contact with neighbours. If you have school age children you are likely to regularly meet other parents. The boundaries of these relationships are to do with place, such as location of housing, and context, such as parenting and education.

In the course of your life you will form a variety of relationships which are more or less significant. Some may last for decades; others may end, with varying degrees of grief (or even relief), after a short period. While there is much talk of 'relationships' on daytime television and in the problem pages of magazines and newspapers, it is less than clear what relationships are for, which criteria can be used to assess them, how different types of relationships are characterised and how roles connect with relationships.

When someone experiences mental distress, their relationships with family, friends or work colleagues may change. Hilary, for example, spoke of the changes to her relationship with both her partner and her work colleagues. New relationships may be formed with other service users/survivors and with mental health workers. As with all relationships, those formed in the world of mental health services will vary a great deal and be characterised in various ways. Some relationships will be seen as helpful, others as unhelpful; some as caring, others as controlling; some as therapeutic, others as detrimental; some as empowering and others as disabling.

In service user–worker relationships, for example, service users may be excluded from discussions about their care or treatment. Boundaries are erected to include or to exclude and they may be covert or overt, spoken or unspoken. In relation to mental health and distress, boundaries may support what can and can't be done, what can and can't be said, who should do what, and how, where and when. Another aspect of the service user–worker relationship boundary may be protective: for example, workers are not permitted to engage in sexual relationships with service users, nor to share confidential information about a service user without their consent.

There are likely to be different views about the nature and appropriateness of boundaries in any relationship. There may be disagreement about whether they are necessary at all, and about whether and how they should be regulated. The first activity relates these questions to some specific examples. You will revisit the people in this activity throughout the unit.

Activity 3.1 **Relationship boundaries – challenges and opportunities**

30 minutes — Learning outcomes 2, 4 and 5

Read through the stories below and make some notes about what you see as the challenges and boundaries of the relationships or situations described.

Surrinda

Surrinda was admitted to the local mental health hospital acute unit following what was considered to be a serious overdose. She now finds she is always accompanied by a nurse, who stays within arm's length of her, and she is not allowed to leave the hospital. Surrinda wonders how this is supposed to help her.

Errol

Errol works as a support worker in a community residential home for people who experience mental health difficulties. Errol says, 'I live for my job,' and socialises with service users/survivors. Sometimes they stay at his house and Errol talks to them about his personal problems. He sees this as being open and honest.

John

John is a mental health social worker who has experienced severe depression. He is just about to go back to work in the mental health team and considers how his personal experience will affect his relationships with service users/survivors and colleagues.

Rhiannon

Rhiannon is a service user/survivor who for some years has been attending a local voluntary sector drop-in where she is also a voluntary worker. She has made some very good friends there. One of them, Gill, tells her that she has taken an overdose as she does not want to go on any longer. Rhiannon is not sure what to do for the best.

Comment

These are one course tester's comments about challenges and boundaries:

- Surrinda: professional responsibilities versus individual freedom; power imbalance; intrusive observation may be the opposite of therapeutic intervention; lack of trust.
- Errol: conflict of role; leaves himself open to allegations; overburdening service users/survivors; failing in role as professional.
- John: questions how he will be able to cope; what will others think; what about 'professional detachment'?
- Rhiannon: risk of losing Gill's trust; risk of feeling guilty if something happens; need to act quickly; impact of her own experiences.

Several course testers were concerned about Errol: they thought that he was breaking professional boundaries and that service users/survivors had enough to do coping with their own problems, without being burdened with Errol's. What challenges did you identify for Rhiannon? Do you think there is a 'right' answer in her case? Perhaps there isn't one, and it is only by considering the complexities that boundaries present that you begin to find a way through them. This activity has given you a taste of some of the challenges that arise in relationships in mental health services, which you will continue to explore throughout this unit and the rest of the course.

The experience of mental distress may also challenge relationships outside services. For example, people may feel under the surveillance of family members who are concerned about relapse. Families may agonise over what to do for the best when someone stops taking medication, and employers may wonder how to approach a valued employee who seems to be taking on more and more when their level of mental distress is increasing. However, this assumes that everyone has relationships with family members and friends. Sometimes this is not the case and the lack of relationships in itself may cause difficulties.

So, what are relationships for? It has been suggested that relationships enable us to fulfil our basic needs. Abraham Maslow (1970) is probably best known for outlining a hierarchy of needs (Figure 3.1).

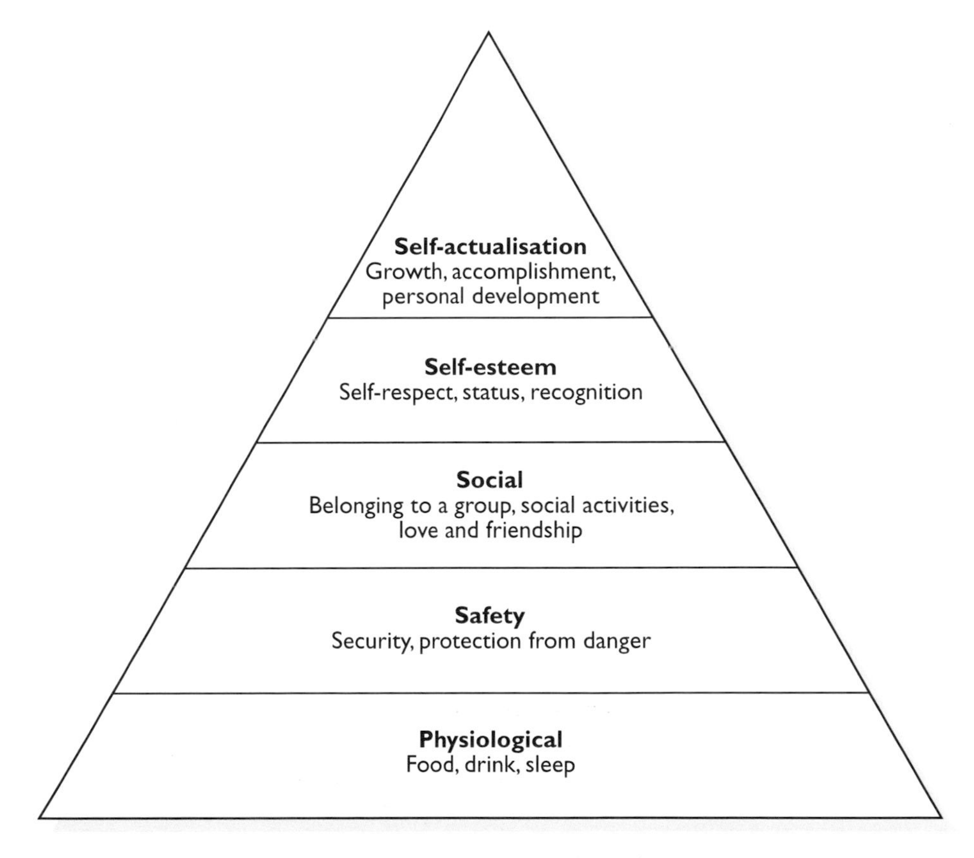

Figure 3.1 Maslow's hierarchy of needs (Source: based on Maslow, 1970)

In Maslow's model, 'lower order' needs have to be satisfied before 'higher order' needs can be fulfilled. If, for example, you are feeling tired, hungry or unsafe you may be unable to participate fully in your K272 tutorial group, or in life more generally! The next activity enables you to think about how the hierarchy of needs relates to relationships.

Activity 3.2 **Relationships and needs**

30 minutes Learning outcome 1

Look through Maslow's hierarchy of needs. Write down how a relationship could contribute to, and detract from, the satisfaction of each of the levels of need. Are some kinds of relationship more significant than others at different stages in the model and at different times of life? Start at the bottom of the hierarchy and work your way up.

Comment Course testers thought that the first two needs were basic to everyone and that in the first instance were provided (though not always) by parents for children. In adult relationships some people may be financially dependent on another, for example a non-working partner, so the relationship will be central to meeting their needs. Relationships were thought to be important at all levels: although it is possible to eat, drink and sleep while having only minimal relationships with other people, it would be difficult to meet other needs without them. The relationships people have in the home may undermine safety, for example in abusive relationships. Moving up the hierarchy, relationships play an increasingly important role in the way they can both enable and prevent the meeting of needs.

As you will have seen from this activity, it is not always the case that relationships contribute to the satisfaction of needs. Sometimes your experience of relationships, whether with family members, friends, colleagues or professionals, may leave you feeling diminished and undervalued. Abusive or negligent relationships have the potential to thwart the achievement of needs and to create new ones – for love, security and safety, for example. So, relationships are crucially significant in their impact on your wellbeing. This has been acknowledged by the Mental Health Foundation:

> The pivotal role of relationships in affecting well being was also a key theme of research into user groups and drop-ins. This highlights the importance of feeling part of something, of knowing there are others who have been through similar experiences.
>
> (Mental Health Foundation, 2001)

So, what helps in relationships? Wright *et al.* (2001) found that while stigma and discrimination may have a negative impact, acceptance is the foundation of a supportive relationship. Relationships will vary a great deal: some may be described as 'personal', others as 'professional', and it is sometimes difficult to make this distinction. So, how might they be assessed? It has been suggested that relationships can be considered on the basis of the following eight dimensions (Duck, 1992):

- **content of interactions** – what people do together, the types of activities engaged in
- **diversity of interactions** – the range of activities engaged in
- **qualities of interactions** – assessed by examining the intensity and style of interactions, the non-verbal signals exchanged, and so on
- **relative frequency and patterning of interactions** – how often people meet or contact each other
- **reciprocity and complementarity** – the reciprocal nature of actions in the relationships; for example, if you invite someone for a coffee, they are likely to say 'it's my turn' next time

- **intimacy** – two kinds are identified, physical and psychological; as relationships develop, access to intimacy generally increases
- **interpersonal perception** – the way one person's perception of another either matches or mismatches the other person's perception of themselves
- **commitment** – determination to continue and respect a relationship in the face of adversity or temptation.

It may be helpful to consider these dimensions and the way some may be more prominent than others in particular relationships. However, describing and attempting to assess the quality of a relationship is one thing; agreeing on what is appropriate – and deciding on what 'appropriate' means in the first place – is quite another.

Take Errol's situation from Activity 3.1, for example:

> Errol works as a support worker in a community residential home for people who experience mental health difficulties. Errol says, 'I live for my job,' and socialises with service users/survivors. Sometimes they stay at his house and Errol talks to them about his personal problems. He sees this as being open and honest.

Errol is a worker who appears to have close relationships with the service users/survivors he works with. Possibly there is a good deal of reciprocity and complementarity in their relationships, and perhaps psychological intimacy; there is no indication of physical intimacy. But it is not clear what the service users/survivors think of the arrangement or whether Errol's behaviour is appreciated or not. Is his self-disclosure welcome or not? Do the service users/survivors feel privileged or burdened by it? He appears committed to his job, but is it a healthy commitment? It seems that there is a blurring of personal and professional boundaries between Errol and those he works with. As you will see in Section 6, professional boundaries are subject to regulation and have a pivotal place in ensuring that relationships and roles are not harmful.

3 Roles and relationships

You have the potential to play multiple roles in your life. These roles often position you in relation to other people and imply certain things about what you do. As a parent or an informal carer, there is an expectation that you will provide physical and emotional care to your children, relative or friend. As a student on K272 you are expected to progress through the course, read the units and complete the assignments. As a service user/survivor of mental health services there may be an expectation that you will comply with the care and treatment offered. As a mental health worker you are expected to comply with the terms of your job description and to adhere to professional guidelines. Roles may change over time: a child grows up and becomes independent; a worker may gain promotion and assume a managerial position. A worker may become a service user/survivor. A service user/survivor may become a mental health worker. Roles concern what people do, how they behave in relation to others and how people relate to them in that role.

Activity 3.3 **Roles and relationships**

15 minutes

Learning outcome 1

Under the headings 'Role', 'Relationship' and 'Challenges', list the roles you play in your everyday life, how these connect with a relationship or relationships and any challenges you have encountered.

Comment

One course tester listed his roles as follows.

Role	Relationship	Challenges
Partner	Partner	Having to attend family gatherings
Friend	Friends	Knowing whether to confront behaviour I'm not happy about
Nephew	Family	Acting as a carer – it's getting in the way of our strong relationship
Consumer	Service providers	Feeling I have little choice; concerns about the environment
Musician	Fellow musicians	Differences in taste
Social worker	Professionals	Different approaches
	Service users	Care versus control
Course tester	Unknown writers	Takes up spare time; less time with partner

Another course tester wrote:

> Conflicts between home and work life are the most relevant. The responsibilities of both can sometimes cause friction when there is not enough time to manage everything.

Although your list will reflect your own situation, there are several challenges that affect roles and relationships:

- role conflict
- role ambiguity
- role incompatibility
- role blurring.

Rhiannon's situation shows examples of these challenges:

> Rhiannon is a service user/survivor who for some years has been attending a local voluntary sector drop-in where she is also a voluntary worker. She has made some very good friends there. One of them, Gill, tells her that she has taken an overdose as she does not want to go on any longer. Rhiannon is not sure what to do for the best.

Role conflict occurs when someone is expected to carry out more than one role in the same situation. Rhiannon has the role of friend, in which loyalty and respect for choice are likely to be paramount, as well as the role of volunteer worker. Did Gill tell her as a worker or as a friend? When there is uncertainty about roles, role ambiguity may occur. In Rhiannon's situation there may be a lack of clarity about the scope of her responsibility, her role, other service users/survivors' and workers' expectations of her performance, and the evaluation of her work. She may be uncertain about what the role of 'friend' requires in a situation such as this.

Role incompatibility happens when expectations of roles are clear but there is a mismatch between people's expectations. For example, if the drop-in has particular rules about disclosure, Rhiannon's worker role may be incompatible with her role as a friend who values confidentiality. Role incompatibility is similar to role conflict. However, conflict suggests that some kind of resolution is possible, whereas incompatibility seems to imply that there is no way through the challenge presented by the incompatible roles. Role blurring (and even role reversal) can occur when a worker talks about their personal troubles to service users/survivors. Some people may argue that this is not necessarily unhelpful, depending on the circumstances and relevance of the worker's problems to the service user/survivor. Brandon (2001), talking about enabling practice, gets quite close to advocating an increased blurring of roles. However, this is a contested area, to which you will return in Section 6.

Relationships are bounded by the roles people perform within them. One element within relationships between workers and service users/survivors that appears to have a clear boundary is power, and you consider this next.

4 Power and relationship boundaries

Within mental health practice in particular, there is a power imbalance in relationships between workers and service users/survivors. Put at its starkest, workers have the power to forcibly medicate and detain service users/survivors against their will by implementing mental health legislation. Service users/survivors have no such power. In the 1960s Goffman highlighted power structures that existed in what he called 'total institutions'. He gives a graphic illustration of power dynamics in a state mental hospital at that time:

> The authority of the attendant in the operation of his control system is backed up by both positive and negative power. This power is an essential element in his control of the ward. He can give the patient privileges, and he can punish the patient. The privileges consist of having the best job, better rooms and beds, minor luxuries like coffee on the ward, a little more privacy than the average patient, going outside the ward without supervision, having more access than the average patient to the attendant's companionship or to professional personnel like the physicians, and enjoying such intangible but vital things as being treated with personal kindness and respect.
>
> The punishments which can be applied by the ward attendant are suspension of all privileges, psychological mistreatment, such as ridicule, vicious ribbing, moderate and sometimes severe corporal punishment, or the threat of such punishment, locking up the patient in an isolated room, denial or distortion of access to the professional personnel, threatening to put, or putting, the patient on the list for electro-shock therapy, transfer of the patient to undesirable wards, and regular assignment of the patient to unpleasant tasks such as cleaning up after the soilers.
>
> (Goffman, 1961, p. 54)

Goffman highlights examples of power in institutions. Some commentators consider that the power inherent in large institutions has been transferred to community settings such as group homes. But what form does power take?

Dowding (1996) writes of two concepts of power: 'power to' and 'power over'. 'Power to' has been described as 'outcome' power, meaning a person's ability to bring about (or help to bring about) outcomes. An example might be a service user/survivor's decision to tell family and friends about their mental distress. 'Power over' has been described as 'social' power and involves someone's ability to use incentives to bring about a desired outcome. One way of thinking about incentives is as a 'carrot and stick' approach. In other words, people may respond to positive incentives such as praise (the carrot) or to negative incentives such as threats of punishment (the stick), but either way the person who has 'power over' uses the incentives to get the outcome they want. Dowding points out that achieving an outcome by using power over others can be done in either blatant or subtle ways. He describes incentive structures which involve the full range of benefits and costs that arise from behaving in one way rather than another. Goffman's examples of the power of the attendant in the 1960s mental hospital are quite blatant. There are also examples, from as recently as the 1980s, of 'token economy' schemes, where cigarettes were awarded for good behaviour (Kay Sheldon, personal communication).

In mental health services, the exercise of social power is wide ranging. For example, professionals may 'take over' a situation, preventing what a service user/survivor sees as self-determination and autonomy, under the guise of helping (however well intentioned), and so perpetuate a paternalistic power relationship. The power of professionals is bolstered by mental health legislation. There may be an implicit or explicit recognition that behaving in one way rather than another will result in implementation of legislation and compulsory detention. For instance, someone may know that if they refuse to go into hospital as a voluntary patient they will be admitted formally, under mental health legislation. This is a situation of some concern, as the experiences of people interviewed by Henderson (2002, p. 39) illustrate:

> **Elaine**: Yes, I've been sectioned, but I can't remember how many times. I think maybe two or three, I'm not sure. Because what's happened is that several times I've been more or less told I've been unofficially sectioned. You're told go in or be sectioned – so what's the choice?
>
> **Teresa**: At the end of the three days I was given the option of I could either stay voluntarily or if I decided not to stay voluntarily then they might section me again, so I said okay, I'll stay voluntarily.

It has been suggested that in community settings the power imbalance may be more in the service user/survivor's favour (Muir-Cochrane, 2000). This assertion is, however, questionable. While people have the power to refuse aftercare services, they may still be formally removed from the community and detained in hospital. The introduction of community treatment orders (as part of proposed changes to mental health legislation in England and Wales at the time of writing – June 2004) may further challenge the assertion by ensuring that aftercare – which could include treatment – is given under compulsion in the community.

Relationship boundaries are, however, often ambiguous; their limits are unclear and people are uncertain about how best to proceed. One of the most challenging issues in terms of boundaries and power – personal, professional, emotional and physical – is continuous, close observation. In the next section you explore this in more detail.

5 Challenging relationships

Mental health practice is fraught with uncertainties, ambiguities and paradoxes. One practice which illustrates this acutely is constant or continuous observation.

5.1 Continuous observation

Observation is a method of 'managing' people who are considered to be at risk of harming themselves or others. In acute wards of psychiatric hospitals continuous observation is a common response when people are thought to be a risk to themselves or others. But just what does observation entail? There are different levels, often known as baseline, intermittent and continuous. Baseline observation is where staff are aware of people's whereabouts, and intermittent observation involves staff checking on a service user/survivor's whereabouts at regular periods, for example every 30 minutes. With continuous, sometimes known as constant, observation people may be accompanied at all times by a nurse who stays within arm's length. Observation is usually undertaken by nurses, and the Scottish Executive (2002, Section 3.2) has pointed out that the task should not be seen as a 'low level' or less skilled one.

Activity 3.4 **Observing observations**

1 hour

Learning outcomes 2 and 3

You may have direct experience of continuous observation, either as a service user/survivor or as a worker, or it may be new to you. Whichever is the case, you may find the content of this and the following activity distressing. Please bear that in mind as you plan your work.

Turn to Reading 4 by Bowles *et al.* in the Resource File and make some notes on formal observations and boundaries from the perspectives of the authors, who have different roles in the mental health system.

Comment

Course testers identified several different perspectives on observation that explicitly and implicitly refer to the concept of boundaries. For example, from the psychiatrist's point of view there may be boundaries of power between professions; continuous observation represents a boundary between care and control. For the service user/survivor there is a boundary between truth and injustice, between guilt and status, and between dignity and infantilising or degrading and intrusive practices. The nurse presents a rationale for continuous observation – if all else has failed – and concentrates on the emotional containment that it may provide.

So, continuous observation affects everyone involved, yet may also depersonalise what are, physically at least, close relationships. It might feel that something intended by professionals to be therapeutic is experienced as degrading and voyeuristic, even though they appear to be searching for ways of ensuring people's safety.

What might be done to meet the challenges posed by continuous observation? Elsewhere in the article (not reproduced in Reading 4) the authors suggest three ways in which practice could be improved. First, workers need to consider whether they have done everything possible before or instead of observation. Second, they advocate a bridge between risk management and risk taking, rather than a focus on risk elimination. Finally, they suggest that nurses who undertake observation should have a central role in deciding the levels of intervention. On an optimistic note, they suggest that:

> It is not beyond the realms of possibility that patients may also contribute to this discussion and also experience increased trust and personal responsibility.
>
> (Bowles *et al.*, 2002, p. 259)

The article is powerful in itself, in the way it draws together the views of people involved in continuous observation. The next activity explores the impact of observation in more detail.

Activity 3.5 **Too close for comfort?**

1 hour Learning outcomes 2 and 3

Listen to the discussion on track 1 of the audio where you will hear Charis, a service user/survivor, and Siobhan, a nurse, talking about their experiences of formal observation. Pay particular attention to examples of power, boundaries and challenges, and reflect on what is said about them.

Then relate the following questions to yourself:

1 What would it be like to be observed in this way?
2 What would it be like to observe and follow another person around in this way?
3 What might be good about it?
4 What might not be so good about it?
5 How helpful are boundaries?

Comment A course tester wrote:

> I would feel totally dehumanised by the experience but I think it's also degrading for the observer. It puts people into roles and relationships that might not sit naturally with them. It might keep people safe, but it also seems to put barriers between people, whether other workers or other patients. It seems that the professionals are more concerned with the end result, rather than how they get there.

Another course tester thought this activity was very challenging. She wrote:

1. At first I would feel acutely self-conscious and unable to be myself in any ordinary way. An overwhelming sense of invasion and lack of space would make me fearful and passive, then maybe aggressive and angry because of the hopelessness and powerlessness of the situation – where to be passive and 'good' is clearly the order of the day. I would wonder what was expected of me by them – counter to all that it is to be an adult. I would be concerned about the effect of this bizarre attention on others around me and would worry that staff might be frightened of me and my sexuality. I would find it very hard to be assertive about staff I might not like and who breached boundaries or expressed views by which I felt challenged or joined in with my personal conversations. I hope that to survive I would be able to create a mental space to tune out this control – I might feel even more determined to find ways to sabotage the situation, even if this meant a focus on self-harming in order to escape such a regime. I can imagine too that I would become very constipated and sleepless and withhold from friends and others around me. Infantilised probably sums it up best for me.
2. I would feel very conscious of the unnaturalness of the situation and concerned that this is a highly responsible, intense and yet short-term role. It is fraught with ambiguities that have care and control blurred in a context that might have life-threatening or life-saving consequences. If I found myself with someone with whom I felt seriously uncomfortable, I would need to express this for the benefit of both of us because the situation would be too stressful and unhelpful. Would I want the observed person to conform and not be distressed? How would they want me to be? What if I am unacceptable to them or they act on their feelings and self-harm or attack me out of frustration – would this be a professional failure?

   If I don't know the person, what relationship possibilities exist in this setting where I have the power to watch, hear and smell everything about them? I would be concerned to be discreet about bathing and toileting and seek to be passive yet present when others are engaged with them.

   The challenge of risk taking would seem to have little place here, although there could be potential through dialogue and conversation if some trust is established, and human rights, respect and dignity aren't eclipsed in the name of perceived dangerousness. The needs and demands of others would also be a challenge – both colleagues and service users – and I guess I would tune out and focus on my primary task and role with all its attendant paradoxes, not least of which might be 'why'?
3. The positive aspects of continuous observation might include the opportunity to offer and spend quality time with someone on their journey and to really be able to make a difference, or at least offer some safety and support. If there is regular contact a trusting and caring relationship might emerge with the prospect of some continuity that is often not possible in mental health settings. From the perspective of the observed, they too might feel safer and more able to go with their own flow if the observer can strike the balance between enabling and protecting. Where clarity and agreement about purpose are well framed, it might follow that the experience is more tolerable and even helpful.

4 It might be very unhelpful if the observed and observers don't get on. A sense of alienation and isolation can be increased when so much attention is being given and received – resentment of others. There could be inappropriate sharing of information, irritating and inappropriate habits and behaviour such as sleeping or preaching. This is basically abuse of power in an already highly imbalanced context. Not knowing the observed person or why they are in this situation will add to the negativity and frustration. No space to be you, as both parties are on show to each other.

5 Given that many boundaries are forfeited in this context, those that remain become more heightened and of vital importance, challenging an observer to consider the ethics of each aspect of their interactions. The example of the book is a useful visual boundary, and the sleeping shift seems almost absurd until you hear that toenails can be clipped! 'Other people's shoes' is a relevant mantra here and could lead to sensitive practice where the options are so limited and constrained by custody.

Paradox is a thread that runs through this course tester's response, and it is the paradox of the situation that Charis and Siobhan also identified. From the audio, for example:

For	Against
Valuing of life	Whose life is it anyway?
A 'holding space'	May be perceived as a punishment
Can foster mutual respect	Diminishes privacy and dignity
Can be therapeutic	Is custodial/antitherapeutic
Person feels 'special'	Person feels like a child
Emotional intimacy	Physical intrusiveness
Safety and protection	Deprivation of liberty and autonomy
Supportive	Exploitative
Intensive worker involvement	Lack of continuity and interest

There are no clear-cut answers to the dilemmas and challenges presented by continuous observation. For example, Siobhan has concerns that agency nurses are frequently used to undertake observation but they tend not to form relationships with patients. On the other hand, Charis had some very good relationships with agency nurses. However, one issue is certain: the example of continuous observation highlights clearly the concept of power in relationships and the challenge of relationship boundaries in mental health services. Charis certainly felt that continuous observation had kept her alive: an outcome of not being on continuous observation might have been, for her, suicide.

5.2 Workers who become service users/survivors

One additional aspect not included in the audio extract was Charis's experience as someone who has worked in mental health services. She brought her experiences as a worker into her new role as a service user/survivor, and was able to draw on those experiences to help her through a very difficult period in her life. Workers are just as likely to experience mental distress as anyone else. The impact on professional relationships was something that Rufus May, a clinical psychologist who was diagnosed with schizophrenia when he was 18, noted in an audio interview:

> Because I am open about my own experiences of madness, for some people they would question my validity as an expert practitioner, as a 'sanity consultant'. There is a big expectation among professionals to be that – to be models of sanity – and I question that. Distress is something we all experience.

Service users/survivors have much to offer the world of work. So are there any implications for people as they start or return to employment?

Consider John's experiences:

> John is a mental health social worker who has experienced severe depression. He is just about to go back to work in the mental health team and considers how his personal experience will affect his relationships with service users/survivors and colleagues.

John's experiences on his return to work may be complex. Brandon (2001) found that nurses had a particularly difficult time. In his study of the experiences of nurses being treated for depression, one nurse commented:

> I keep mental health problems hidden from nursing colleagues as much as possible. I find mental health, nursing professionals and society as a whole vindictive, critical and judgmental.
>
> (Brandon, 2001, p. 10)

Social workers appear to have a slightly less difficult time. Stanley *et al.* (2002), in their research into the effects of the workplace on depression in social workers, found that 47 per cent of workers said colleagues who knew about their depression were supportive or tolerant.

In Unit 2 you read about the idea that the whole is more than the sum of its parts. This applies to everyone, whether in the role of worker or service user/survivor. Holism includes the idea that physical sickness is not solely pathology of the body and that mental distress is not simply a dysfunction of the brain. One of the dimensions of holism you have not encountered so far is the significance of healing (you will also come across debates about recovery in Module 4). One view of healing is that:

> [it] involves the engagement of the healer with the patient's mind and emotions as well as physical symptoms, an understanding of their relationship with their inner self and social environment. The healer is therefore required to undertake an empathic exploration of many different facets of experience; the practitioner–patient relationship cannot be reduced to a subject–object relationship. [...] An idea that is commonly found in this kind of holistic discourse is that of the 'wounded healer'.
>
> (Deverell and Sharma, 2000, p. 35)

This view challenges the boundaries between the personal and the professional, between service user/survivor and worker. The view is that they are, rather, 'fellow sufferers' (Deverell and Sharma, 2000, p. 36). Hopton (2002) does not use the word 'sufferer'. Instead he talks about 'experts by experience' and argues:

> What many mental health professionals lack is the experience of being in severe distress and not knowing when that emotional and psychological pain will end, or the experience of living with a close friend or relative who is having that kind of experience.
>
> (Hopton, 2002, p. 8)

In this way, personal experience of distress can be an advantage when working with people who may be experiencing similar difficulties. The worker may be better able to empathise with the service user/survivor and understand what they are going through, although their relationship is a professional one. On the other hand, sometimes powerful or distressing experiences can prevent people from working with others who have been through similar situations. In other words, holistically, all experiences make us who we are.

So, as a mental health social worker, John will have additional knowledge based on his personal experiences. However, when he is working with service users/survivors, he is doing so as a worker, not as a friend or fellow service user/survivor, and must adhere to the ethical guidelines that seek to regulate relationship boundaries.

6 Regulating relationship boundaries

Up to now in this unit you have focused more on what *is* the case and considered, for example, what power means, what relationships are for, and what the implications of crossing boundaries are. This section focuses more on what *should be* the case. What are the ethical issues involved in the regulation of boundaries? Who should regulate relationship boundaries? Returning to the four people you encountered in Section 2, you may remember discussion about Surrinda, who is continuously observed in the interests of her own safety but whose liberty is severely restricted; the appropriateness of Errol's relationships with service users/survivors; John crossing the boundary from worker to service user and back again; and Rhiannon, who was unsure of what to do for the best in relation to her friend and fellow service user/survivor.

'Appropriateness' suggests a right way to proceed, and it may be that you found yourself saying, 'It depends,' because it often seems there is no one right way. So how then do you decide how to proceed, to do the right thing? Where do you find guidance about appropriate boundaries in relationships? You might say that you manage quite well in regulating your relationships without guidance. However, there are special issues which arise in relation to worker–service user relationships. The imbalance of power and the possibility of exploitation make some regulation necessary. There is a need for openness and transparency where relationships are concerned.

Professional documents or codes, statements of values and legislation all provide helpful guidance. For example:

From a voluntary sector project:

> Our ethos is based on *respect* for each other so that we all have the opportunity for participation whatever our role and relationship with the organisation.
>
> (Redcar and Cleveland Mind, 1999)

From the General Medical Council:

> You must not allow your personal relationships to undermine the trust which patients place in you. In particular, you must not use your professional position to establish or pursue a sexual or improper emotional relationship with a patient or someone close to them.
>
> (GMC, 2001, p. 9)

From the Nursing and Midwifery Council:

> You must, at all times, maintain appropriate professional boundaries in the relationships you have with patients and clients. You must ensure that all aspects of the relationship focus exclusively upon the needs of the patient or client.
>
> (Nursing and Midwifery Council, 2002, p. 4)

From the British Association of Social Workers:

> To set and enforce explicit and appropriate professional boundaries to minimise the risk of conflict, exploitation or harm in all relationships with current or former service users, research participants, students, supervisees or colleagues.
>
> (BASW, 2003)

From the General Social Care Council:

> In particular you must not:
>
> 5.4 Form inappropriate personal relationships with service users.
>
> (GSCC, 2002)

Although they do not give specific guidance on what is considered acceptable or unacceptable, these guidelines and statements are based on values: that is, they make some basic assumptions about what is – and therefore what is not – acceptable or appropriate.

A web-based conference in 2003 on the role of values in mental health proposed a 'National Framework of Values for Mental Health' that:

- recognises the role that values play in shaping the views and attitudes of individuals, within and across all stakeholder groups
- develops the means of identifying and addressing the diversity of values held by individuals within and across all stakeholder groups
- identifies the 'given' values that are essential to the partnership process and that all stakeholders need to sign up to
- protects the heritage and knowledge of all stakeholders in the partnership process.

Underlying the conference was a belief that:

> Values in mental health reflect and interact with values in society as a whole. But values are particularly important in the field of mental health with its complex interplay of issues around trust, power, responsibility, risk, safety, 'duty of care' and service user empowerment.
>
> (NIMHE Values Project Group, 2002, p. 1)

Writing about the National Service Framework (NSF) for Mental Health in England, Fulford *et al.* (2002) note that the NSF standards are overtly values-based. However, there is little reflection in the NSF on the:

> planning, delivery and commissioning of services where the values embodied by these standards come into conflict. For example:
>
> - user-centred values. A key theme that runs through the NSF is the user-centred approach. But 'users', like any other group of people, are very far from being homogenous. They present a diverse range of personal and collective values relating to their beliefs, aspirations, cultural backgrounds and lifestyles, as well as their experience and understanding of mental health problems and expectations of services. So an 'acceptable' intervention for one and a 'good' outcome may be unacceptable for another
> - values and teams. Another key theme in the NSF is the emphasis on multi-disciplinary teams. Again, teams are very diverse. Different team members have different skills, but they also have different values: a social worker may be concerned with risk, for example, a nurse or psychiatrist with compliance and a manager with client throughput. Mental health organisations themselves have different corporate values that may not be shared by other agencies or accord with those of their staff or users and family members.
>
> (Fulford *et al.*, 2002, p. 25)

In this extract Fulford and his colleagues are introducing a number of challenges that you will encounter as you work through the course. For example, in Unit 4 you consider your own culture, whether personal or professional, in Module 3 you consider different types of intervention, and in Module 4 you return to regulation, but of mental health services as a whole rather than individual workers or professions.

7 Conclusion

This unit has considered some of the many complexities, uncertainties and dilemmas that exist in mental health. Relationships, and roles within them, are a source of both great support and equally profound distress for many people. By confronting some of the dilemmas presented by working with and within relationships in mental health you have considered the values and boundaries that seek to regulate relationships. There is no single 'right' answer about how Surrinda, Errol, John and Rhiannon should act or respond to their situations and relationships, although there are some things they must not do, and clear guidelines about how relationship boundaries should be regulated.

Through the accounts given by Charis and Siobhan, this unit has explored the significance and place of power in relationships as well as the practical impact of physical boundaries through close observation. It seems clear that a holistic approach needs to incorporate an understanding of roles and relationships and balance the dilemmas they may present.

References

Bowles, N., Dodds, P., Hackney, D., Sunderland, C. and Thomas, P. (2002) 'Formal observation and engagement: a discussion paper', *Journal of Psychiatric and Mental Health Nursing*, Vol. 9, pp. 255–60.

Brandon, D. (2001) 'Wounded healers', *Openmind*, Vol. 108, Mar/Apr, pp. 10–11.

British Association of Social Workers (2003) *Code of Ethics for Social Work*, www.basw.co.uk/articles.php?articleId=2 [accessed 13/08/03].

Deverell, K. and Sharma, V. (2000) 'Professionalism and everyday practice: issues of trust, experience and boundaries' in Malin, N. (ed.) *Professionalism, Boundaries and the Workplace*, London, Routledge, pp. 25–46.

Dowding, K. (1996) *Power*, Buckingham, Open University Press.

Duck, S. (1992) 'What are we trying to develop when we develop a relationship?' in Giddens, A. (ed.) *Human Society*, Cambridge, Polity Press, pp. 23–5.

Faulkner, A. and Layzell, S. (2000) *Strategies for Living: A Report of User-led Research into People's Strategies for Living with Mental Distress*, London, Mental Health Foundation.

Fulford, K.W.M., Williamson, T. and Woodridge, K. (2002) 'Values-added practice', *Mental Health Today*, October, pp. 25–7.

General Medical Council (2001) *Good Medical Practice*, 3rd edition, London, GMC.

General Social Care Council (2002) *Codes of Practice for Social Care Workers and Employees*, London, GSCC.

Goffman, E. (1961) *Asylums*, Harmondsworth, Penguin.

Henderson, J. (2002) 'Experiences of "care" in mental health', *Journal of Adult Protection*, Vol. 4, No. 3, pp. 34–44.

Hopton, J. (2002) 'The limits of professionalism', *Openmind*, Vol. 118, Nov/Dec, p. 8.

Maslow, A. (1970) *Motivation and Personality*, New York, Harper & Row.

Mental Health Foundation (2001) *Real Life Evidence in Mental Health*, www.mentalhealth.org.uk/page.cfm?pagecode=PRAR0115 [accessed 27/01/04].

Muir-Cochrane, E. (2000) 'The context of care: issues of power and control between patients and community psychiatric nurses', *International Journal of Nursing Practice*, Vol. 6, No. 6, pp. 292–9.

National Institute for Mental Health in England Values Project Group (2002) *Consultation Document on a National Framework of Values for Mental Health (draft long version)*, London, NIMHE.

Nursing and Midwifery Council (2002) *Code of Professional Conduct*, London, NMC.

Redcar and Cleveland Mind (1999) *Code of Conduct*.

Scottish Executive (2002) *Engaging People: Observation of People with Acute Mental Health Problems*, www.show.scot.nhs.uk/sehd/publications/opam/opam-02.htm [accessed 26/03/04].

Stanley, N., Manthorpe, J., Brandon, D. and Caan, W. (2002) 'Down on record', *Community Care*, 17–23 Jan, pp. 38–9.

Tronto, J.C. (1993) *Moral Boundaries: A Political Argument for and Ethic of Care*, London, Routledge.

Wright, S., Faulkener, A. and Bird, L. (2001) 'A friend in need ...', *Openmind*, Vol. 109, May/June, pp. 14–15.

Unit 4 Culture, Ethnicity and Mental Health

Contents

You will need:

Resource File:

Reading 5 'The roots of racism in psychiatry'

Audio 1 'Shifting boundaries'

Learning outcomes

After studying this unit you should be able to:

1. appreciate the significance of racism and cultural variations in the meaning of mental health and mental distress
2. understand the importance of working with diversity in mental health services
3. discuss the global impact of psychiatry and psychiatric imperialism
4. identify ways in which developing cultural competence may improve mental health practice and services.

1 Introduction

In the following extract some of the impacts of culture, identity and discrimination are described by Veronica Dewan. Dewan, whom you met in Unit 1, has experienced periods of mental distress associated with the diversity of her family circumstances and the complexity of her experiences. She talks about the impact of racism on her and her adoptive mother:

> I became engaged in an official system of care at birth, a system that denigrated my Indian heritage, a system that made meaningless my true identity. It was my first encounter with social services in 1957 at six weeks of age – an illegitimate, 'mixed race', hard-to-place baby.
>
> Adoption is made of fairytales. The innocent young woman has a brief passionate encounter with a dark handsome stranger, crossing barriers of religion, culture, 'race' and class. She becomes pregnant and the father denies paternity. The mother is told she has committed a terrible sin and, worse than being an unmarried Catholic, she has been sullied by a Black man and has brought shame upon herself. [...]
>
> And what of the adoptive mother? [...] We lived in a rural area of southern England where my adoptive mother encountered unrelenting hostility because she was Irish. It persisted at home where my English adoptive father frequently made anti-Irish jokes. [...]
>
> I started to trace my biological parents in 1979, and met them in 1985 within a few weeks of each other. As a child I was told I was Indian but nothing more. It was only when I met my biological father that I learnt he was an Indian Punjabi Hindu, with Pathan heritage. Meeting my Irish birth mother was both joyful and painful. I was ecstatic with happiness to be meeting her but made distraught by her racist view of my paternal heritage.
>
> (Dewan, 2001, pp. 44–5)

In this unit you consider mental health and distress and their relationship to the culture of people, communities and nations. UK society is often said to be 'multicultural', that is, made up of many different groups, each with a different culture, living and working side by side. However, most societies draw on a range of cultural roots and traditions, and culture is not static, but constantly changing and developing. In the first part of the unit you consider explanations and definitions of terms such as 'culture', 'race' and 'ethnicity', and the impact of institutional racism in mental health services. You then go on to assess the challenges posed by developing a culturally diverse response to experiences that are often labelled as mental illness, and how particular models and explanations of mental illness have been imposed on people across the globe. Finally, you consider the development of cultural competence as a means of improving mental health practice and services.

2 Whose definition is it anyway?

What did you think about the experiences Dewan described? She mentions the way her 'true identity' was made meaningless. Do you think there is such a thing as a single, and possibly static, identity that shapes who we are? In Unit 2 you read about Hilary, and the various identities she had as a teacher, woman, professional, partner, friend, feminist and gardener. Dewan also mentions several identities – child, woman, daughter, adopted daughter and someone with an Indian heritage (which itself has several aspects). She says that her biological heritage is important to her, but that racism has impacted on her in several ways. Within her family, her adoptive mother experienced racism as a result of her Irish heritage, while her biological mother held racist views about Dewan's biological father.

In 1992 Suman Fernando discussed racism and psychiatry in a key article in *Openmind*, the Mind magazine (this is reproduced as Reading 5 in the Resource File if you would like to read it). In it he identifies historical connections between racism and psychiatry on several fronts. Links between the biomedical focus of psychiatry and biological explanations of 'race' are particularly strong. Fernando suggests that because of those links psychiatry developed practices that are racist by virtue of a focus on biologically determined characteristics. He also argues that developing 'multicultural awareness', also known as multiculturalism, is not always helpful, as it may obscure the realities of racism experienced by some service users/survivors.

However, it is important to be clear about the terms and concepts that Fernando and Dewan use. For example, Dewan mentions race, culture and heritage. Fernando talks about multiculturalism. This section sets out to find a way through some key concepts and terms, but with a note of caution – none of them is clear-cut, and much more could be said about them. Whole books have been written about each one. As you work through this section, try to apply the concepts to yourself as preparation for the first activity.

2.1 Race and racism

Dictionaries and glossaries are helpful places to start when looking for explanations of concepts. These are some of the definitions of 'race' found by an internet search engine:

> A classification that is not typically chosen but instead assigned by others; defined most often by physical characteristics.
>
> People who are believed to belong to the same genetic stock.
>
> A family, tribe, people, or nation belonging to the same stock; a class or kind of people unified by community of interests, habits, or characteristics.
>
> One of the great divisions of mankind, having certain physical peculiarities in common. The term is often used imprecisely; even among anthropologists there is no generally accepted classification or terminology.

How helpful are the results of that search? Is race a useful concept when you think about yourself? Race is sometimes seen as a natural and neutral method of grouping people according to physical characteristics, but using the term may perpetuate racist ideologies. On the other hand, the term 'human race' may suggest a single, unifying collection of people. The concept of race as a biologically determined entity recognisable by external appearance has been dismissed in scientific circles as a basis for categorising people. As Rose *et al.* (1984) state:

> Human 'racial' differentiation is indeed only skin deep. Any use of racial categories must take its justification from some other source than biology.
>
> (Rose *et al.*, 1984, p. 127)

The genetic diversity *within* populations is, Giddens (1989) argues, as great as that *between* populations. Giddens goes on to say that:

> There are clear physical differences between human beings and some of these differences are inherited, but the question of why some physical differences, and not others, become matters for social discrimination and prejudice has nothing to do with biology.
>
> (Giddens, 1989, p. 246)

Racism is not just about personal prejudice: it is a doctrine characterised by the behaviour of individuals and institutions, based on the concepts of racial difference (Fernando, 1992) and the belief that some races are superior to others. Racism affects people at all levels, whether individual, interpersonal or societal.

Another complication is that the word 'race' is often confused with the concept of culture. People seen as racially different are assumed to have different cultures, so that value judgements attached to 'race' become transferred to 'culture' (Fernando, 2002). When racism is implemented and practised through the institutions of society, sometimes without the people involved even being aware that they are being racist, it is called 'institutional racism'. The Stephen Lawrence Report (Home Office, 1999) defined institutional racism as:

> The collective failure of an organisation to provide an appropriate and professional service to people because of their colour, culture or ethnic origin. It can be seen or detected in processes, attitudes and behaviour which amounts to discrimination through unwitting prejudice, ignorance, thoughtlessness and racist stereotyping which disadvantages minority ethnic people.
>
> (Home Office, 1999, p. 26)

A leaked copy of a report into the death of a black patient in a regional secure unit also found institutional racism within the NHS. The *Guardian* newspaper reported:

> The NHS is riddled with institutional racism and persistently fails to give patients from the black and minority ethnic communities the services they need and deserve.
>
> (Carvel, 2004, p. 1)

So when you consider race you need to be aware of the impact of racism.

2.2 Ethnicity

In the UK the term 'ethnic' may be taken to mean a mixture of cultural background and racial designation, the significance of each being variable. For example, ethnicity has been seen as a mixture of 'culture, religion, skin colour, language and family origin' (Fernando, 2002, p. 13).

Another internet search came up with the following definitions for ethnicity:

> The ethnic group or groups that people identify with or feel they belong to. An ethnic group is defined as a social group whose members have the following four characteristics:

- share a sense of common origins
- claim a common and distinctive history and destiny
- possess one or more dimensions of collective cultural individuality
- feel a sense of unique collective solidarity.

Of or pertaining to combinations of race, culture, nationality and/or religion.

The cultural practices, language, cuisine and traditions used to distinguish groups of persons – not biological or physical differences.

Identification with, and feeling part of, an ethnic group, and exclusion from certain other groups because of this affiliation.

From these definitions it seems that ethnicity is something that describes both belonging and not belonging. If we belong to one particular ethnic group, are we excluded from others? Ethnicity refers to a psychological sense of belonging which will often be cemented by similar physical appearance or social and cultural similarities. This sense of belonging to a group can either stigmatise individual members or empower them (MacLachlan, 1997). Viewed from this perspective, ethnicity is a potentially discriminatory concept. Although ethnic groups provide a sense of belonging, they also function as gatekeepers in excluding the 'others'. As you read in Unit 1, 'otherness' can be a very unpleasant state.

2.3 Culture and multiculturalism

One result of societies becoming multicultural is that the view of what culture means has changed. So, back to the internet. What does a search for the word 'culture' produce?

A people's whole way of life. This includes their ideas, their beliefs, language, values, knowledge, customs, and the things they make.

The entire way of life of a defined group of people, which includes the interrelated spheres of the physical world, material social conditions, ideology, spirituality, affect.

Learned behavior of people, which includes their belief systems and languages, their social relationships, their institutions and organizations, and their material goods – food, clothing, buildings, tools, and machines.

Behaviour peculiar to homo sapiens, together with material objects used as an integral part of this behaviour. Thus, culture includes language, ideas, beliefs, customs, codes, institutions, tools, techniques, works of art, rituals, and ceremonies, among other elements.

The integrated pattern of human knowledge, belief, and behavior that depends upon man's capacity for learning and transmitting knowledge to succeeding generations; the customary beliefs, social forms, and material traits of a racial, religious, or social group; the set of shared attitudes, values, goals, and practices that characterizes a company or corporation.

Is there a difference between culture and ethnicity? It seems that culture is something that is learned, and you could learn about the beliefs and languages and customs that make up a particular culture. Does that mean you could become part of that culture? If you wanted to describe the 'culture' of, say, working-class people in the north east of England, or Belfast Protestants, or Turkish Cypriots in London, you might include the ways in which people celebrate ritual events such as weddings and funerals, the stories and songs that have been handed down within the community, how members of the community dress and, more importantly, the ways in which these practices embody the community's shared ways of thinking about itself and the world.

Fernando (2002) suggests that culture may refer to 'conceptual structures' that determine the total reality of life within which people live and die – a flexible system of values and world views by which people live, define their identities and negotiate their lives. Societies are 'multicultural' if they consist of more than one cultural group; however, not all multicultural societies adopt 'multiculturalism'. The most common pattern of multicultural societies is one majority and several minority cultures. Multiculturalism is based on the theory that the promotion of understanding of each other's culture reduces the unfounded fears of the majority cultural group in any given society, thus reducing inequalities, discrimination and conflict. Multiculturalism promotes the value of diversity and insists that all cultural groups should be treated equally and respectfully.

But is it that simple? As Dewan's experiences illustrate, it may lead to stereotyping, and not take into account the reality of people's lives. Cultures are often presented as static, equally applicable to everyone within them. Multiculturalism fails to acknowledge the levels of acculturation, that is, the ways in which cultures change over time and as a result of contact with other cultures, particularly as regards the descendants of migrants. However, changes over time may also be influenced by the impacts of (un)employment, education, housing, gender, age and class. So, although multiculturalism aims to promote the value of diversity by focusing on cultural differences, it hides the *similarities between*, as well as the *diversity within*, cultural groups.

Another aspect of culture that is often overlooked is institutional culture. An organisation may have a culture that draws from the various professional cultures that are part of it. Likewise, specific professions may influence the culture of organisations, bringing yet another meaning to the word 'culture'. For example, when applied to the culture of a group or organisation such as 'police canteen culture' or the 'culture of psychiatry' the word culture means:

> the ethos or ways of functioning of a system or a group of people in a particular context.
>
> (Fernando, 2002, p. 10)

In care settings culture often means 'the way we do things here'. Over time, people who belong to particular groups or communities develop shared ways of doing and thinking about things. Similarly, the members of organisations – including health and social care organisations – develop habitual routines and rituals for 'getting the job done'. They also develop a shared sense of the meaning of their joint activity, which entails the development and maintenance of shared values. Over time, these shared ways of acting, talking and thinking become embedded in the life of the organisation, whether at a formal level in mission statements, procedures and guidelines, or at a more informal level as 'the way we do things here'.

2.4 Cultural relativism

The final concept in this section is 'cultural relativism'. Cultural relativism proposes that all points of view are equally valid and that all truth is relative to the individual and their environment. All ethical, religious, political and aesthetic beliefs are truths that are relative to the cultural identity of the individual. Cultural relativism reflects the idea that various approaches to wellbeing and illness have merit and should be equally acceptable, as each culture has its own reasons for its behaviours and decisions.

When taken to its extreme, cultural relativism implies that there are no universal values. Pat Bracken, a psychiatrist who spent some time working with survivors of war in Uganda, found that an awareness of cultural relativism was essential in his work and that:

> decades of experience from development work (with very mixed results) should alert us to the dangers of inserting non-indigenous frameworks and priorities into situations where communities are attempting to reconstruct their lives and ways of life.
>
> (Bracken, 2002, p. 15)

Cultural relativism has been criticised as it appears to be incompatible with international human rights which are based on *universally* accepted values. However, a universal declaration of human rights could also be criticised from a cultural relativist position in that it emphasises the human rights of individuals, rather than those of families or communities. (Human rights legislation, especially in mental health, is a complex area and is the subject of Unit 22.) Although a flexible approach to cultural relativism promotes cultural sensitivity, some care workers are faced with dilemmas when having to care for people whose practices and traditions they do not agree with, such as female genital mutilation, male circumcision and arranged marriages.

At this point you may be glad to begin applying concepts in real life! So, your focus now shifts from abstract concepts and definitions to practical implications for how you live and work. You start with a person you know well – yourself.

Activity 4.1 **Making concepts real**

30 minutes Learning outcome 1

Using the headings race, ethnicity and culture, write a short paragraph about each as they apply to you. You might like to do your own internet searches for definitions of the terms, although this is not essential for the activity.

Comment One course tester wrote:

> I find it very difficult to separate out culture and ethnicity and then separate them from the person I am. At first I thought of where I came from (place) and my local area (council estate). I was brought up to respect authority, be polite and speak when spoken to. My mother did not have paid work – indeed, my father told her when they married that he was 'now her life's work'! My culture was structured along the lines of class and gender. Now I think of my culture in relation to place and heritage, but who I am has been shaped by class.
>
> When I started to think about ethnicity as a combination of culture and race at first I didn't see any examples of race. I thought about trips to south east Asia, particularly a small island off the coast of China, where my partner and I were the only people who looked western. Then I began to think about the box I usually tick on questionnaires and surveys – 'white'. Often I don't say someone is a white woman, I just say a woman. But what does white mean?

So, there may be regional variations within a broader national culture and some aspects of 'race' may not be identified as such – for example, 'whiteness'. Terminology can structure the way people see themselves; for example, the use of the term 'minority' suggests that there is a corresponding majority. If the word 'ethnic' is applied only to groups of colour, such as African, Asian and African-Caribbean people, white ethnicities are invisible: whiteness becomes the silent norm.

2.5 Racism revisited

Language, terms and explanations do not simply reflect differences in ethnicity; they also have a role in producing difference (Gunaratnam, 2000). You have already encountered explanations of racism in general terms, but what of racism and mental health practice? At the beginning of this section you read about the article by Fernando (reprinted as Reading 5) on the history of psychiatry and racism. Fernando was writing in 1992. An article in the same publication ten years later suggests that things have not improved a great deal. Robert Jones says:

> Black people [...] are detained within the psychiatric system and prescribed medication by staff who allow their own racist stereotypes (such as 'big, Black and dangerous') to affect their thinking, diagnosis and choice of treatment.
>
> (Jones, 2002, p. 19)

Despite several reports into racism within the psychiatric system, Jones argues, things have not changed dramatically, and while there has been a movement for change in the wider mental health arena, it has amounted to little more than 'treading water' for black people. Jones goes on to say:

> It is a disgrace that in 2002 Black people within the mental health system are in much the same situation as we were in the 1990s. The difference now is that our situation attracts very little attention.
>
> (Jones, 2002, p. 19)

Jones is suggesting the mental health services in the UK are not responsive to the needs of black people. However, there are indications that this may be changing, in England at least. In March 2003 the National Institute for Mental Health in England (NIMHE) produced a document called *Inside Outside: Improving Mental Health Services for Black and Minority Ethnic Communities in England*. In the foreword the then minister for health, Jacqui Smith, notes that the government is determined that mental health services should be non-discriminatory and appropriate to the needs of people who use them. However, she goes on to acknowledge that:

> the testimony of many service users, carers and members of the black and ethnic minority communities is that this aspiration is not yet a reality. [...] Tackling ethnic inequalities within mental health services, in terms of prevention, early detection, access, diagnosis, care and quality of treatment and outcome is one of the greatest challenges facing us. We have an obligation to meet this challenge and tackle racism and institutional discrimination within our health services.
>
> (NIMHE, 2003, p. 3)

It remains to be seen how successfully the challenge will be met. The author of the report, Sashi Sashidharan, is concerned that the Department of Health has tried to minimise the significance of what was being said in the report:

> The experience of working with the DoH around this document, and subsequently, has reinforced my view that this is an example of institutionally racist attitudes and behaviours on its part.
>
> (Cited in Leason, 2003, p. 8)

One thing is certain: this is a complex and challenging area and, as some minority groups are more likely than others to come into contact with mental health services, it deserves close attention. But what of the international place of mental health and the impact on mental health services in the UK? The next section moves to locate the points Fernando and Jones make in a wider, global context.

3 A bigger picture

'Globalisation' is a word that is increasingly being used about culture and ethnicity (although it also has a specific economic meaning in relation to multinational corporations' power to transcend national borders). Cultural globalisation is the interaction of ideas from the cultural traditions of various parts of the world coming together as if into an open marketplace (Ritzer, 2000). For example, McDonald's burger bars are to be found across the globe, from Moscow to Bangkok. Sushi bars are common in New York and Buenos Aires as well as in Japan. Global media outlets such as MTV, a popular music television channel, tailor the style of programmes to suit different cultures although retaining a specific western flavour. Economic power is very important in this context, and often the overt exercise of such power by companies, nations and groups of nations plays a significant part in determining the outcome of globalisation. In the field of mental health one outcome is that particular ideas and ways of thinking tend to be dominant across the world, irrespective of their usefulness or appropriateness to individual cultures.

The dominant ideas are generally referred to as 'western' and include medical and psychiatric explanations of mental illness (Fernando, 1992). But notions of 'eastern' and 'western' are debatable and value-laden, particularly politically orientated notions of 'western models'. Western is often equated with white, European and developed, and is contrasted with non-western, eastern, non-white and non-developed or 'third world'. Where are the dividing lines between east and west? Are New Zealand 'west' and Albania 'east', for example? There is likely to be cultural diversity between northern and southern Italy; between people from Scotland and Greece; between Japanese and Chinese people. The terms 'western' or 'eastern' are examples of stereotyping and may be problematic in the way they present a simplified picture of the world.

This process has a long history. Globally, the current approach to mental health is based on knowledge within western psychology (the study of the mind) and psychiatry (the study of disorders of the mind). Psychology and psychiatry developed together between the 18th and early 20th centuries and are products of world views, attitudes and beliefs characteristic of Western European and American culture as it was during those years. The two disciplines are highly ethnocentric to the culture in which they developed, although it has been assumed that they have universal relevance. So, for example, a global approach assumes that disorders or symptoms identified in one culture would be replicated and hold the same meanings in another. One way of explaining the global impact of psychiatry is through 'psychiatric imperialism', the subject of the next activity.

Activity 4.2 **Psychiatry rules, OK?**

45 minutes

Learning outcome 3

Turn to track 2 on Audio 1 and listen to Suman Fernando talking about the global imposition of what he terms 'western' models of psychiatry. As you listen, make some notes on any examples of power, diversity and interconnections that Fernando makes. After you have heard the discussion, think about what impact psychiatric imperialism may have had on you.

Comment A course tester who has used mental health services commented:

> Psychiatric imperialism impacts on me by denying me choice, by its approach to depression as an illness to be treated through drugs. So I'm defined and labelled and have to be passive while the drugs take their course. There's no one I can tell my story to without fear. If I want to try other approaches I need money and courage and risk rejection or even loss of liberty. If I dare to be different, will this also be judged as mad and pathologised?

Psychiatric imperialism seems to have stifled diversity and imposed treatments linked to diagnoses that ignore spiritual and cultural contexts. Fernando certainly appears to see the power of psychiatry as widespread, and instrumental in developing what he calls western approaches to mental illness across the world. The example he gives is of the increase in the diagnosis of depression in Africa. He links this with the impact of the globalisation of the pharmaceuticals business, a topic you will explore in more detail in Unit 20. However, he goes on to note that imperialism is not all negative and suggests that there have been some benefits. He makes connections between many different approaches to helping people who experience mental distress, but warns about the dangers, as he sees them, of interventions becoming big business and being sold to the public as commodities.

One constant throughout the development of the disciplines of psychiatry and psychology is that mental health problems continue to be discussed and presented in psychological and psychiatric publications in terms of illness rates. Psychiatric diagnoses are contested and may not be as objective as, for example, diagnoses such as angina or pneumonia. Fernando has argued that what 'fits' in one place may not be relevant in another. A book known as the International Classification of Disorders (ICD) (WHO, 1992) contains details of illnesses and is used by doctors to help diagnosis. The book is regularly updated, and gives details of all current disorders and diseases, their symptoms and diagnoses. It could be described as a recipe book for illnesses.

Universality of diagnosis underlies the ICD. Diagnosis attempts to make sense of a range of human problems from a *medical* angle. To move towards understanding mental health and distress from a holistic perspective requires a very much wider approach than that usually taken by western psychiatry and psychology. But even then, what is understood by 'mental health' is not necessarily the converse of illness, whichever way illness is conceptualised or defined.

In 2001 the World Health Organization (WHO) made mental health the subject of its annual special report. Countries across the globe were assessed on their progress in mental health service provision according to whether they had mental health legislation and policies and the percentage of total budget spent on mental health. The ten recommendations for action are that countries should:

1. provide treatment in primary care
2. make psychotropic drugs available
3. give care in the community
4. educate the public
5. involve families, communities and consumers
6. establish national policies, programmes and legislation
7. develop human resources
8. link with other sectors
9. monitor community mental health
10. support more research.

To help guide countries, the report provides three scenarios for action, which reflect the varying levels of national mental health resources around the world:

> Scenario A [...] applies to economically poorer countries where such resources are completely absent or very limited. Even in such cases, specific actions such as training of all personnel, making essential drugs available at all health facilities, and moving the mentally ill out of prisons, can be applied. For countries with modest levels of resources, Scenario B suggests, among other actions, the closure of custodial mental hospitals and steps towards integrating mental health care into general health care. Scenario C, for those countries with most resources, proposes improvements in the management of mental disorders in primary health care, easier access to newer drugs, and community care facilities offering 100% coverage.
>
> (WHO, 2001, p. xiii)

By presenting the three scenarios the WHO acknowledges the differences between countries (although not necessarily those within them). However, there is a particular medical – Fernando would argue 'western' – slant to the scenarios. Many people prefer to use traditional or indigenous systems of medicine for all sorts of problems, including those seen as 'mental'. Such forms of development or intervention do not appear to be included in the scenarios proposed by the WHO. The most popular system of indigenous medicine in India and Sri Lanka is Ayurveda, which means 'the science of life' (Frawley, 1989); in China people turn to traditional Chinese medicine (TCM) (Hammer, 1990), and a variety of systems prevail in African countries (Ademuwagun *et al.*, 1979). In Sri Lanka, for example, it is relatively common for people with mental health problems to consult both Ayurvedic physicians and western-trained psychiatrists. At the same time, and if they can afford it, people go to fortune tellers and *kattadiyas* who arrange for ceremonies for healing and exorcism (Kapferer, 1991).

It appears, then, that people may use several different forms of help when they are feeling distressed or unwell. The use of psychiatric and herbal medication combined with spiritual help fits well within a holistic model, especially when the forms of help are developed in the context of your own culture.

So far in this unit you have looked at concepts and definitions, and have begun to explore racism in mental health and the global impact of western models of mental illness. In the following section you move on to consider the problems in making assumptions about cross-cultural differences and how the development of cultural competence may be a way forward.

4 Cultural diversity and cultural competence

You have already considered the danger of stereotyping based on culture or ethnicity, or explanatory frameworks such as 'east' or 'west'. Stereotypes affect individuals, communities and countries, and Fernando (1992) argues that the concept of mental health must be seen in the relevant political, social and historical context. The context includes stereotypes of mental health and illness and what they represent, as well as of 'race', culture and ethnicity. Pride in your ethnic and cultural heritage may be important for mental wellbeing in a context where racism undermines self-confidence and feelings of self-worth (Akbar, 1981). This is something that Dewan, whose account you read at the beginning of this unit, found very difficult to achieve for many years.

Pride in racial heritage is something that some Irish people may find difficult to maintain when Irish people are often stereotyped as mad or funny (Mind Information Unit, 2001). On the other hand, some people derive great pride from their Irish heritage. There are many similarities between the experiences of Irish people and black people when they come into contact with racism and mental health services. Everyone makes assumptions and uses stereotypes some of the time. It is one way to make sense and order out of life and events.

Some stereotypes have long histories: for example, as the basis of a rhyme that portrays Welshmen as untrustworthy. Humour is often steeped in stereotype: the bluntness of people from Yorkshire or the meanness of the Scots, for example. The video you watched in Unit 1 uses stereotypes of mental health professionals to make some serious points. However, there are dangers in accepting or using stereotypes carelessly. By finding out more about particular groups of people there is also the risk of creating stereotypes of all people within that group. You have already encountered this with multiculturalism. The next activity enables you to consider both stereotypes relating to yourself and those you apply to others.

Activity 4.3 **Making assumptions**

30 minutes

Learning outcome 1

Read the extracts in Box 4.1 from the Mind factsheet about the mental health of Irish people in Britain, and make some notes on the stereotypes it identifies.

If you are Irish, write a few sentences about the impact that any of the stereotypes have had on you. If you are not Irish, write a few words about any stereotypes as they may apply to you in your particular circumstances.

Then make a note of any assumptions you have about any group of people and how you might find out more about them.

Box 4.1 Mind factsheet on the mental health of Irish-born people in Britain

The Irish experience in Britain

Many Irish-born people, on their arrival to Britain, despite being white and English speaking, experience culture shock, alienation and racism. A sense of loss and feelings of alienation are common experiences shared among all minority groups. As with other minority groups the combination of social and cultural needs increases the likelihood of mental distress. The colonial relationship between Ireland and England has shaped the beliefs and the behaviour of Irish people and contributed to feelings of inferiority which are easy to reject in Ireland, but more difficult to 'throw off' living in England. Such conflicts occur when Irish people are confronted by negative stereotypes. They are faced with the choice of either ignoring or confronting them. Either way can be a recipe for distress.

Most ethnic monitoring programmes do not contain a separate category for Irish people. The net result is that the Irish community continues to be excluded from attempts to tackle discrimination in Britain. [...]

Racism

The social conditions of Irish-born people and of people from other ethnic minority communities must be considered in any assessment of the health of these communities. It has been established and proven that Irish-born people face discrimination in the fields of employment, health, housing and education.[1] This means that like other minority ethnic groups, Irish-born people are often denied access to, or given second rate opportunities in these areas. These conditions must contribute to mental distress. [...]

Diagnosis and assessment of mental ill-health

Diagnosis may be based on prejudice, lack of cultural understanding and stereotypical assumptions such as 'mad Irishman' and 'alcoholic' making them questionable. There is anecdotal evidence from Irish voluntary sector agencies that alcohol is also used by some Irish-born people as a form of self-medication when the symptoms of depression or schizophrenia make life difficult. This can result in a diagnosis of alcoholism with the underlying disorder being neglected. As in the case of the African Caribbean person, who is likely to have a secondary diagnosis of cannabis psychosis, the Irish person is likely to have a secondary diagnosis of alcoholism.[2]

As with some other communities religious devotion is often misinterpreted by practitioners, who do not understand the significance of prayer and religious rituals for some Irish clients. There is also a tendency to blame mental illness on 'Irish catholic guilt' thus making the assumption that all Irish people are of the same faith. It also neglects both the reality of exclusion and disadvantage and the importance of faith and prayer to people in distress.

Although Irish-born people speak English, the language is sometimes used differently and can be misconstrued by professionals assessing the client. Despite legislation to deter racist abuse, it is still common for accents or colloquialisms to be ridiculed. This may evoke an angry response, and thereby confirm the negative stereotype assumptions that the perpetrator believes.[3]

References

1 *The Irish in Britain* Commission for Racial Equality (1997)

2 Walls, P (1996) *Researching Irish Mental Health: Issues and Evidence – A study of the mental health of the Irish community*. A Muinearas Report

3 Tilki, M *The Health of the Irish in Britain*, Federation of Irish Societies

(Source: Mind Information Unit, 2001)

Comment One course tester from south west England identified stereotypes of Irish people as stupid (because of their accent), aggressive, mad, alcoholic and religious. She went on to say:

> I wasn't sure any of the stereotypes applied to me until I got to the accent stereotype. I have a strong regional accent and although almost fashionable now, accents were not acceptable in the past. A colleague who has no trace of a regional accent said recently that he often feels that his lack of an accent now stereotypes him.

Several course testers mentioned stereotypes about gender in relation to men – 'Lad culture, I'm supposed to like cars' and 'A man should like football, hate cooking and play golf.'

The factsheet itself has a stereotype of Irish people – that they are white. Do you have to be white to be Irish? And what about travellers? In Northern Ireland travellers are defined and included as an ethnic group in the Race Relations (NI) Order. An important point to note is that diagnoses are subject to assumptions and biases inherent in the psychiatric system as well as those held (often unwittingly) by the person making the diagnosis. The disproportionate diagnoses of schizophrenia in young African-Caribbean men is an example of this. Diagnoses may easily reflect cultural misunderstandings and racist stereotyping, as well as a host of other factors such as gender, age and social class. In other words, the western, medical model of mental illness is as much a product of assumptions and biases as is the individual practitioner who is implementing that model. In Unit 6 you will return to the impact of stereotypes and stigma on people who use mental health services.

The excessive diagnosis of a particular illness in an ethnic group could be the result of cultural misunderstanding, institutional racism or both. The diagnosis itself may be inherently 'correct' in having been arrived at through the usual process, but still be of limited usefulness, or inappropriate or damaging to the individual. In other words if, for example, a young African-Caribbean man is diagnosed as having schizophrenia, account needs to be taken of the context in which the diagnosis is made rather than it being accepted as an 'objective' reflection of an underlying condition.

One challenge, it seems, is to meet and communicate with people in a way that recognises the similarities and differences between everyone, whether as individual worker, service user/survivor, student, teacher or a combination. The rest of this unit will look at how this may be achieved by the model of cultural competence developed by Papadopoulos *et al.* (1998), shown in Figure 4.1. It was devised to help health care workers respond sensitively to patients, but is also relevant to you, whether or not you work in a health or social care setting.

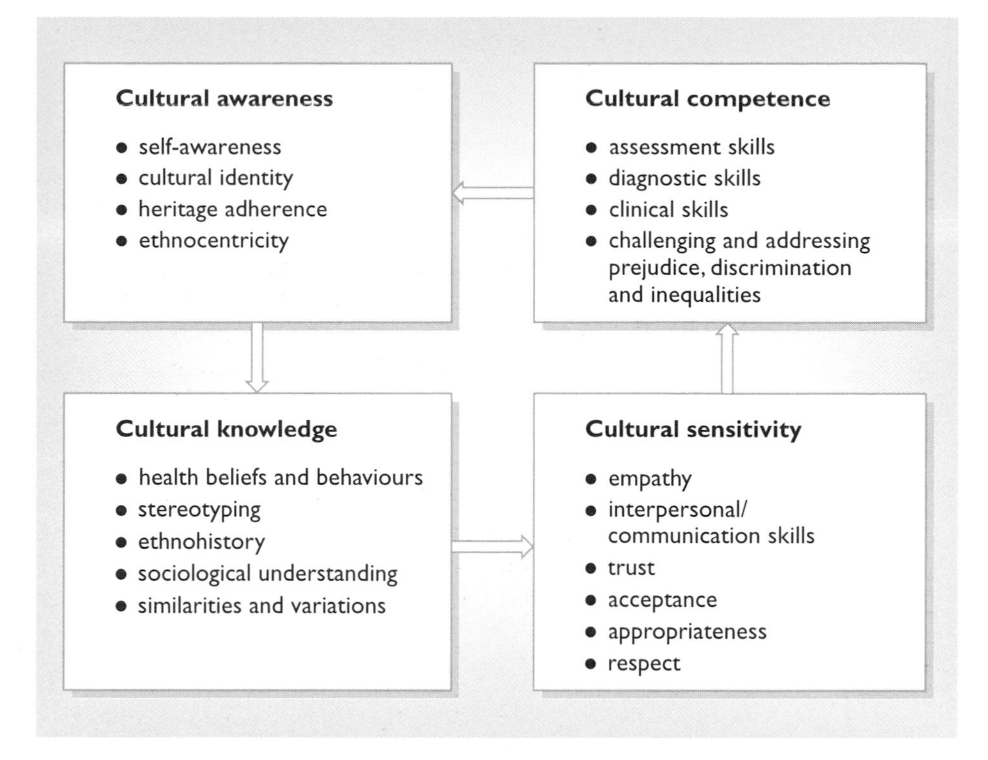

Figure 4.1 Cultural competence (Source: Papadopoulos *et al.*, 1998)

The first stage in the model is *cultural awareness*, which begins with an examination of your personal value base and beliefs. Understanding the construction of cultural identity as well as its influence on your mental health beliefs and practices is necessary to developing cultural competence. You have already started this process with the work you did for Activity 4.1.

Cultural knowledge, the second stage, can be gained in a number of ways. Meaningful contact with people from ethnic groups different from your own can enhance your knowledge of their mental health beliefs and behaviours as well as increase your understanding of the problems they face. This is a two-way process, as others may learn about your beliefs as well. An important element in achieving *cultural sensitivity* (the third stage) is the way professionals view people in their care. Dalrymple and Burke (1995) state that unless people who use services are considered as true partners, culturally sensitive care is not being achieved; to regard them otherwise means that professionals are using their power in an oppressive way. Equal partnerships involve trust, acceptance and respect as well as facilitation and negotiation.

The achievement of the fourth stage (*cultural competence*) requires bringing together and applying awareness, knowledge and sensitivity. A most important component of this stage of development is the ability to recognise and challenge racism and other forms of discrimination and oppressive practice. This model differs from multiculturalism in recognising that by developing cultural competence you are able to consider specific cultural issues between and within groups.

Activity 4.4 **Cultural competence**

45 minutes Learning outcome 4

Turn to track 3 of Audio 1 and listen to Rena Papadopoulos and Suman Fernando talking about cultural competence. You might find it helpful to have a copy of the model with you as you listen. Make some notes on each of the stages. How helpful do you think this model is? What challenges does it pose?

Comment A course tester who works in a mental health setting commented:

> The cultural competence model attempts to promote understanding and improvements in mental health practice and service delivery. The experiences of minority groups and cultures in the psychiatric system leave a lot to be desired and anything that attempts to improve things is always welcome. But these problems have been with us for a long time and this model, like others before it, will not change them. Models like this suggest stages and progressions. As individuals we all learn in different ways. I've never found this type of model useful. My development and progression has come from exposure to people and situations and the exchange and challenge of ideas. Maybe there are people who this might inspire or affect.

Another course tester, a receptionist in a health centre, wrote:

> I found this model really useful, especially in helping me look at my own culture, although I still worry about stereotyping and making assumptions about people. I also think that it will be difficult for me to make changes when my workmates haven't heard of this way of working.

A course tester who works at a drop-in centre wrote:

> I think this model fits with the holistic model. It suggests that the individual is the starting place and at the heart of understanding and in this respect it mirrors the holistic model. Cultural knowledge moves us on to consider a wider environment in relation to communities, be they friends and family, neighbourhoods, the workplace or other organisations and structures.
>
> Cultural competence links theory to practice in a professional/care-giving context, which isn't seen as an end in itself but as part of an overall holistic approach. On the other hand, the model is rather clinical and uses academic and sociological language rather than everyday language.

So, course testers had a variety of responses to the model. Papadopoulos *et al.* (1998) argue that cultural competence is developed as a result of people gaining awareness, knowledge and sensitivity about diverse cultural identities. What do you notice about the model? First, it is a model about *developing* cultural competence and this suggests a process, probably over quite a long time. This is an important point. There is always more to know and learn. The model was developed with health care workers in mind, so skills, often known as competencies, are framed in that way – assessment, diagnostic and clinical skills. However, these are skills everyone uses in one way or another, even though they may be called something else. For example, when you meet someone for the first time you may think about whether you would like to get to know them more, or whether they are interesting or hard to understand. Although what you are doing is not a structured social work, medical or nursing assessment, it is still an assessment and so has the potential for making assumptions and stereotyping.

From your 'assessment' of your new acquaintance, you may decide you would like to meet them again. You reflect on your opinions and experience and come to a conclusion on how to proceed. This is your 'diagnosis'. The model goes on to identify clinical skills as part of cultural competence. How might these skills apply outside health and social care work? They could be the skills you develop in communicating and responding to people – the varied encounters you have in the course of your life. The final element in cultural competence is challenging and addressing prejudice, discrimination and inequalities. This is an essential element and underpins clinical, assessment and diagnostic skills because it involves challenging and addressing discrimination and prejudice in yourself as well as in others.

Activity 4.5 **Developing cultural competence**

1 hour Learning outcome 4

Developing cultural competence is one way that people can respond to the diverse needs and experiences of people within the UK. This activity will help you think about how to develop cultural competence for yourself and how it might improve a service or project you are familiar with.

Look again at your notes from Activity 4.1 and at the first stage of the cultural competence model, 'cultural awareness'. Write a paragraph about cultural awareness as it applies to you.

Turn to the second stage in the cultural competence model, 'cultural knowledge'. Set yourself a date to complete this part of the activity. Think about a culture you would like to know more about and make some notes about how you will gain this knowledge.

Finally, identify what changes would need to take place for a service or project with which you are familiar to become culturally competent.

Comment Course testers found this a challenging activity. One wrote that he struggled with the cultural features that were ascribed to him and that he had numerous cultural identities, including Scottish, Dutch, Irish, German, Catholic, British and European. When it came to finding out about other cultures, testers wanted to know more about Somali and Chinese cultures, for example. However, one course tester noted that as there was diversity within cultures and China was such a huge country, she might need to narrow down her search. Another wrote:

> I think I would like to know more about American culture – how different or similar it is to British culture. We always get put together, but I have a feeling there are more differences than similarities.

Talking about the idea of cultural competence was identified as a start in improving services. One tester suggested that different groups of workers could do short presentations about their professional culture to other workers.

What might a culturally competent service look like? First, it would be one that respected everyone involved in delivering or using the service, irrespective of race, class, gender and culture. An important point here is that the 'us and them' boundary is challenged by this model. The 'us' might be service users, and the 'them' workers. Or the 'us' might be nurses, and the 'them' social workers. Or the 'us' might be white doctors, and the 'them' black doctors. There are endless variations on the 'us and them' theme and the challenge to everyone is to constantly be aware of the 'othering' that takes place.

Lees *et al.* (2002) suggest that for services, perhaps the first step is to ask the following questions:

Ethnic monitoring

- Is ethnic monitoring of all clients undertaken?

Communication and information

- Are all clients and their carers able to communicate with staff in a language they feel comfortable with?
- Are services which clients and their carers may need to use clearly signposted and enquiry points clearly marked?
- Is appropriate information available to clients and their carers/relatives in an accessible format (to facilitate informed choice in their care and treatment)?

Religious and spiritual needs

- Do you make provision for clients, their carers and staff to observe their religious and spiritual beliefs?
- Do you facilitate the spiritual and religious wellbeing of clients, their carers and staff?

Gender

- Do clients have a choice of staff of their own gender, with information made readily available about this option?

Diet

- Do meals meet the religious/cultural requirements of clients, their carers and staff?

General anti-discriminatory training

- Can you demonstrate that steps are being taken to equip staff to respond appropriately to differing individual, social, cultural, religious and other needs of black and minority ethnic users?

Complaints

- Is the complaints procedure accessible to minority ethnic users, including those who do not read English?
- Is ethnic monitoring of complaints introduced and maintained?

Monitoring and audit of service use

- Does the monitoring and audit of service use, processes and outcomes include an ethnic dimension?

Involving users

- Do you have a participation strategy for black and minority ethnic communities?
- Are community(ies) involved in setting and in monitoring standards?

Collaborating with other organisations

- Do you have multi-agency strategies?
- Have you developed links with minority ethnic communities and umbrella organisations (such as Race Equality Councils, Council of Mosques or Gurdwaras)?

Employment

- Are the ethnic origins of all staff known and recorded in a sensitive and confidential manner?

- Are personnel involved in recruitment trained in equal opportunity matters?
- Are anti-harassment and equal opportunity employment policies and procedures in place?

Developing cultural competence is an ongoing process, and for services it will involve changes for individuals and practices. A key issue in making connections across cultural differences hinges on meaning. A single approach is not necessarily the most effective. Rather, it is more important that workers take time and explore the meaning of feelings and experiences with service users/survivors. In building a culturally competent mental health service, the aim is to promote cultural competence and sensitivity and to minimise the effects of racism. Achieving these two aims is complex and not easy to put into practice. It is not simply a matter of enabling 'ethnic matching' by increasing the number of people from black and Asian backgrounds working as professionals (although this may help up to a point), but in changing attitudes, practices and training at all levels of the service or organisation.

5 Conclusion

Many of the terms and concepts you have encountered in this unit are problematic. Particularly challenging are broad terms such as 'east' and 'west', or 'Asian' and 'British'. Within each of the concepts or groups there is diversity and difference. For example, a woman from the north east of England may have lived for many years in Cambodia; a young man living in Cardiff may have been born in Senegal. You are as likely to have traditional Chinese medicine in Liverpool as to be prescribed psychiatric medication in Bangalore. Just as there are many different cultures within what could be termed 'the west', there are many variations within 'the east'. So, although in this unit ways of feeling and different experiences are often described in relation to eastern and western perspectives, remember that within those explanations there are many variations. Whenever you encounter generalisations it is essential to remember the importance of context and diversity within as well as between groups.

In summary, in dealing with people from diverse cultural backgrounds, problems need to be analysed from different perspectives as far as possible. But even more importantly, you need to understand and counteract the power of stereotypes and assumptions that carry racist attitudes and inferences.

References

Ademuwagun, Z.A., Ayoade, J.A.A., Harrison, I. and Warren, D.M. (eds) (1979) *African Therapeutic Systems*, Waltham, Mass., Crossroads Press.

Akbar, N. (1981) 'Mental disorders among African Americans', *Black Books Bulletin*, Vol. 7, No. 2, pp. 18–25.

Bracken, P. (2002) 'Meaning, culture and distress', *Openmind*, Vol. 117, Sept/Oct, pp. 14–15.

Carvel, J. (2004) '"Abscess" of NHS racism exposed', *Guardian*, 6 February, p. 1.

Dalrymple, J. and Burke, B. (1995) *Anti-oppressive Practice: Social Care and the Law*, Buckingham, Open University Press.

Dewan, V. (2001) 'Life support' in Read, J. (ed.) *Something Inside so Strong: Strategies for Surviving Mental Distress*, London, Mental Health Foundation, pp. 45–9.

Fernando, S. (1992) 'Roots of racism in psychiatry', *Openmind*, Vol. 59, Oct/Nov, pp. 10–11.

Fernando, S. (2002) *Mental Health, Race and Culture*, 2nd edition, Basingstoke, Palgrave.

Frawley, D. (1989) *Ayurvedic Healing: A Comprehensive Guide*, Salt Lake City, Passage Press.

Giddens, A. (1989) *Sociology*, Cambridge, Polity Press.

Gunaratnam, Y. (2000) *Terminology, Race and Ethnicity*, discussion paper, School of Health and Social Welfare, The Open University.

Hammer, L. (1990) *Dragon Rises, Red Bird Flies: Psychology and Chinese Medicine*, New York, Station Hill Press.

Home Office (1999) *The Stephen Lawrence Inquiry. Report of an Inquiry by Sir William Macpherson of Cluny*, Cm 4262-I, London, The Stationery Office.

Jones, R. (2002) 'Treading water', *Openmind*, Vol. 114, Mar/Apr, p. 19.

Kapferer, B. (1991) *A Celebration of Demons: Exorcism and the Aesthetics of Healing in Sri Lanka*, Washington, DC, Smithsonian Institution Press/Providence, R.I., Berg Press.

Leason, K. (2003) 'Author of mental health report says government diluted racism findings', *Community Care*, 17–23 July, p. 8.

Lees, S., Papadopoulos, I. and Tilki, M. (2002) 'Organisational Cultural Competence Assessment Tool (OCCATool)' in *Cultural Competence in Action Project*, London, Middlesex University.

MacLachlan, M. (1997) *Culture and Health*, Chichester, Wiley.

Mind Information Unit (2001) *Mental Health of Irish-born People in Britain*, www.mind.org.uk/Information/Factsheets/Diversity/Mental+Health+of+Irish+born+people+in+Britain.htm [accessed 2/4/04].

National Institute for Mental Health in England (2003) *Inside Outside: Improving Mental Health Services for Black and Minority Ethnic Communities in England*, Leeds, Department of Health.

Papadopoulos, I., Tilki, M. and Taylor, G. (1998) *Transcultural Care: A Guide for Health Care Professionals*, Dinton, Wilts, Quay Books.

Ritzer, G. (2000) *The McDonaldization of Society: An Investigation into the Character of Contemporary Social Life*, London, Pine Forge Press.

Rose, S., Lewontin, R.C. and Kamin, L. (1984) *Not in our Genes: Biology, Ideology and Human Nature*, Harmondsworth, Penguin.

World Health Organization (1992) *International Statistical Classification of Diseases and Related Health Problems*, Geneva, WHO.

World Health Organization (2001) *Mental Health: New Understanding, New Hope*, Geneva, WHO.

Unit 5 Relating Mind and Body

Contents

You will need:

Resources:

Reading 6 'Tessa's story'

Reading 7 'Kato's story'

Your computer

Learning outcomes

After studying this unit you should be able to:

1. debate the relationship between mind and body
2. describe and apply models which explain the relationship between mind, body, health and wellbeing
3. explore the relationships between mind and body using the examples of ME (myalgic encephalomyelitis or chronic fatigue syndrome), brain injury and stress
4. appreciate responses to conditions which span the mind and the body.

1 Introduction

The relationship between mind and body poses many fascinating questions. What is the mind? How does the mind relate to the body in general and the brain in particular? Are mind, brain and body inextricably connected? How should we think of the relationship between the mind and the body in relation to mental and physical wellbeing? How might the body contribute to or alleviate mental distress? How might the mind impact on physical ailments? Where is the mind?

In this unit you set out on a challenging quest to find out whether it is possible to answer these questions. Many people have wrestled with them, and come up with at best confusing and imprecise answers. Consider this from Paul Broks, a neurologist who because of his scientific training is highly familiar with the brain. He is fascinated by such questions, because in the material structure of body and brain he cannot locate the self, the mind:

> The illusion is irresistible. Behind every face there is a self. We see the signal of consciousness in a gleaming eye and imagine some ethereal space beneath the vault of the skull, lit by shifting patterns of thought, charged with intention. An *essence*. But what do we find in that space behind the face, when we look?
>
> The brute fact is there is nothing but material substance: flesh and blood and bone and brain. I know, I've seen. You look down into an open head, watching the brain pulsate, watching the surgeon tug and probe, and you understand with absolute conviction that there is nothing more to it. There's no one there. It's a kind of liberation.
>
> (Broks, 2003, p. 17)

Perhaps by the end of the unit you will have begun to share this fascination with the interrelationships of the mind, that abstract concept, and the body, that 'too too solid flesh', and their impact on mental health and wellbeing.

Throughout this unit you will reflect on the stories of two women called Tessa and Kato. Through Tessa's personal account of ME you are invited to consider the challenges of this mysterious, but fairly widespread, condition. In the second account, Kato tells of her experience of brain injury, and you explore what happens to the mind and body, the emotions and the spirit, when the brain is injured.

Finally, you consider stress and how physiological responses can explain it, but also how partial that bodily explanation is.

2 Reflecting on mind and body

If you ask yourself, 'How do I feel today?', how do you arrive at your answer? What do you consult? Your body, maybe. You may have some aches and pains troubling you, although you may not have noticed them until you asked yourself the question. You may also consult your mind, your emotions. Perhaps you feel agitated because you have recently had a row, or have too much to do, or have had to sit in a traffic jam on the way to work. Maybe you are bored; or you could be excited about what you are about to study in this unit! There are two broad dimensions to how you feel. There are bodily aspects – aches and pains, energy levels and so on, and there are also mental aspects – feelings and emotions. Are the two connected? Feeling pain usually makes you feel bad in your mind as well as your body. But feeling low in your spirits may also make you feel low in your body.

So there is clearly a connection between mind and body. Why labour the point? For one thing, mind–body links are not fully accepted by all. Indeed, much of our medical system is predicated on a split between the two. There are facts you can learn about the mind–body relationship – the structure and function of the brain, for example – but there are also issues that benefit from reflection, such as the connections between your mind and your body.

Why reflect? One possible answer is that reflection is a good thing in itself and requires no further justification, in the way that reading novels or listening to music is good. That answer is unlikely to convince many people. But reflection can help improve or change what you do. Blackburn (1999) says:

> Reflection matters because it is *continuous* with practice. How you think about what you are doing affects how you do it, or whether you do it at all. It may direct your research, or your attitude to people who do things differently, or indeed your whole life.
>
> (Blackburn, 1999, p. 7)

To illustrate this he gives the example of the relationship between mind and body:

> Many people envisage a strict separation between mind, as one thing, and body, as a different thing. When this seems to be just good common sense, it can begin to infect practice in quite insidious ways.
>
> (Blackburn, 1999, p. 9)

In relation to the questions explored in this unit, the implications of Blackburn's view are challenging to say the least. How do treatments which are physical and impact on the body – medication, for example – affect the mind? Conversely, is it possible for talking treatments, which focus on the mind, to impact on physical aspects of mental distress?

Activity 5.1 **Mind and body**

15 minutes Learning outcome 1

Consider the following stories. Make some notes on how you think the mind–body connection relates to each of them.

1. Mohan works very hard. He has recently had difficulty sleeping, is aware of his heartbeat and feels very anxious. He worries that he will not be able to meet the next work deadline. His family are concerned and say he is uncharacteristically short-tempered and smokes and drinks more than he should.
2. Angela weighs five and a half stone and her weight is continuing to drop. She thinks she is fat and needs to control her food intake.
3. Michael believes he sees and hears things that other people say are not there. He also fears that his internal organs are rotting and people are aware of the smell. His GP says there is nothing physically wrong with him and refers him to a psychiatrist.

Comment

1. This looks like what could be called stress, with both physical and emotional elements.
2. Eating disorders seem to begin in the mind, the person believing they are too fat even when physical measurement shows this to be far from true, leading to instructions to the brain to refuse food.
3. Michael's mind is telling him that things are wrong with his body even though there is no physical evidence for this.

So, there are conditions, none uncommon, which bridge the mind–body divide. The relationship between mind and body continues to challenge and has direct implications for an understanding of mental health and distress and for the rationale presented for different interventions. One condition that poses particular challenges is ME, often known as chronic fatigue syndrome.

3 Mind–body connections: ME

ME (myalgic encephalomyelitis) or chronic fatigue syndrome is a condition which provokes considerable debate, even passion, about whether its origins are in the body or in the mind. It illustrates the challenges posed to orthodox biomedical health systems by such conditions. Although symptoms and severity vary, people with ME experience chronic and disabling exhaustion which makes it almost impossible to live a normal life, hold down a job, or manage a household. As a 'new' disease, first reported in the 1980s and formally acknowledged as a syndrome in 1988 (Showalter, 1997), its causes have provoked massive controversy. You are first going to hear from Tessa, who has recovered from ME.

Activity 5.2 **The experience of ME**

30 minutes

Learning outcomes 3 and 4

Read Tessa's story in Reading 6. As you read, note Tessa's perceptions of connections between the mind and the body.

Then consider the implications of Tessa's story for family, friends and workers responding to someone with ME. What lessons are there?

Comment

In her story Tessa only hints at some factors that may be relevant to what happened to her. However, she is very clear in her view that ME is a mind–body phenomenon, beginning in the emotions. But when she was experiencing ME she rejected this idea totally. As she saw it at the time, the symptoms were entirely physical. She felt nothing, a phenomenon which she now links to depression, but then led her to believe that she was a normal, happy young woman who had been mysteriously stricken by total exhaustion which virtually brought her life to a standstill for several years. The belief that there must be a physical cause is completely understandable from the way she tells her story. Tessa sees ME as an extension of depression, afflicting people who do not feel able to acknowledge limitations or failure to live up to other people's expectations, so that they carry on until their bodies decide to put a stop to it.

She is emphatic that the physical symptoms are real – and that they need to be taken seriously. Being told 'it's all in the mind' is dangerous not only because of the stigma, but also because it may mean that the physical distress is denied. If it really is all in the mind, then it should be possible to tell your mind to behave differently – something she knows people with ME cannot do.

How could or should relatives and workers respond? Tessa's assertion that their patience is needed is not easily applicable in practice. Yet she did find some things helpful:

- Finding a diagnosis. Tessa found it a relief to know that what she was experiencing had a name.
- Being taken seriously, rather than being told to walk around the block three times.

- Alternative or complementary therapy. The ability of the kinesiologist to offer some ongoing support was helpful, even though not curative.
- Diet. The need to consider diet very seriously also emerges from the account. Again, addressing diet is not a complete cure, but it can help in alleviating some of the physical symptoms.
- Waiting to be ready to accept help. This may be the most difficult advice to put into practice, yet Tessa was adamant about it. Her faith in her therapist was enormous, although, as she freely acknowledges, she was not ready to make use of what the therapist offered until she began to get better and her emotions returned with a vengeance. Tessa could see no way the process could have been speeded up.

Tessa was concerned about telling her story because of the strong feelings explanations of ME might raise. Her analysis is controversial: Tessa sees a psychological backdrop to ME that many people with ME, and the organisations that support them, are passionately opposed to. They are committed to the idea that ME is a physical disease with physical symptoms, and that one day a cure will be found. So suggestions that ME has a psychological cause, or any link with depression, are ruled out by most people experiencing this condition. As David Bell puts it in a guide for doctors:

> Perhaps the most bitter argument surrounding chronic fatigue/immune dysfunction syndrome concerns the role played by depression. [...] The arguments have been bitter because of the conviction and insistence of patients that although emotional symptoms are present in the illness, a primary emotional disturbance is not the cause. [...] Patients are angry and frustrated, interpreting the debate over emotions as a trivialization of their illness and as the explanation for why so little has been done to help them.
>
> (Bell, 1995, pp. 8–9)

Kleinman, a leading medical authority, has said that people should be treated by a doctor, not a psychiatrist, 'to spare patients the ... delegitimisation of their experiences' (quoted in Showalter, 1997, p. 131). In making this recommendation, he appears to be reinforcing the stigma associated with mental distress that people with ME are so keen to distance themselves from.

One of the most intriguing things about ME is its recent discovery. Like other relatively recently named disorders – anorexia and bulimia, post-traumatic stress disorder and attention deficit hyperactivity disorder, all of which sit uneasily and controversially in the space between mental and physical ill health – it appears to have come out of thin air. And why does ME, which is so hard to explain let alone respond to, cause such problems?

3.1 Responding to ME: a professional perspective

'Somatisation' is a word you may hear associated with ME or similar conditions. In medical language 'somatisation' is used to describe the presentation of psychological distress as physical symptoms (Harrison, 2001). 'Psychosomatic' is also used to describe medically unexplained symptoms. Here are two definitions quoted by Harrison:

> the tendency to experience and communicate somatic distress and somatic symptoms unaccounted for by relevant pathological findings, to attribute them to physical illness, and to seek medical help for them.
>
> (Lipowski, 1988)

> chronic [...] physical complaints for which there is no satisfactory organic explanation and for which there is evidence of psychological pain.
>
> (Smith, 1985)

It has been estimated that one in five GP consultations is for a somatising problem (Bridges and Goldberg, 1985). Research shows that, like Tessa, many people talk about physical symptoms but later acknowledge psychological factors (Bridges and Goldberg, 1985), although most take less time than Tessa did to come to that acknowledgement. Conversely, some people may never accept that there is anything psychological in their illness. Why some people describe physical rather than psychological problems is an interesting question. As well as cultural differences in the way people talk about illness, Bridges and Goldberg speculate that it is because people believe they will be taken more seriously by their GP, and that physical symptoms are more acceptable than psychological ones, more worthy of taking up doctors' time. This echoes the point made above about the stigma associated with mental distress, and you will consider stigma in more detail in Unit 6.

One explanation for psychological distress taking physical forms, summarised in Table 5.1, proposes that there are biological, social and psychological triggers. However, it does little to explain why some people respond to this mixture of triggers with what are called somatising symptoms, while others do not.

Table 5.1 Overview of the multicausal model of somatisation

	Biological	Social	Psychological
Predisposing	Genetic	Cultural attitudes and beliefs	Somatising personality
		Childhood experience of illness and patterns [of] family illness behaviour	Low self-esteem
Precipitating	Physical illness	Life event or acute stressor, e.g. bereavement, unemployment, lack of social support	Coping behaviour
	Minor pathology		Interpretation of stressful life events
	Heightened physiological arousal		
Maintaining	Side effects of medical treatment, e.g. iatrogenic effects of prescribed drugs	Effect of the 'sick role'	Psychiatric illness, e.g. depression, anxiety
		Mind–body dualism	Health beliefs
		Repeated tests and investigations	Attributions and beliefs attached to physical symptoms
		Resulting disability	Symptom-focusing

(Source: Harrison, 2001, p. 34)

There are very real problems for workers in responding to ME, for example, because of the way services are also split into 'mind' or 'body' interventions. In the next section you consider why mind–body issues present such a challenge by looking at broad frameworks for making sense of mind–body connections.

4 Frameworks for understanding

One reason for the difficulties posed by syndromes such as ME is that they challenge accepted frameworks for understanding, some of which have been institutionalised into ways of treating ill health. For example, the split between general and mental health nursing and between physicians and psychiatrists assumes that one side treats the body, the other the mind. This position is not common to all healing systems. Many, such as Ayurvedic and traditional Chinese medicine (TCM), do not separate out the dimensions of being or create boundaries between them. All aspects are seen holistically, all potentially relevant to health and wellbeing.

So how did the dominant views in western thought about the mind–body relationship develop? In this section you are introduced to three explanations:

- dualism
- materialism
- interactionism or the human experience view.

4.1 Dualism

The French philosopher René Descartes (1596–1650) is credited with being the father of what is called dualism, the mind–body split, which is very characteristic of western belief and health systems. Descartes meditated on whether he could be sure of anything: perhaps he was being deceived by some 'evil demon' into believing that he had a physical existence. Could he exist without a physical form? He wrote:

> was I not, therefore, also persuaded that I did not exist? No indeed; I existed without doubt, by the fact that I was persuaded, or indeed by the mere fact that I thought at all. But there is some deceiver both very powerful and very cunning, who constantly uses all his wiles to deceive me. There is therefore no doubt that I exist, if he deceives me; and let him deceive me as much as he likes, he can never cause me to be nothing, so long as I think I am something. So that, after having thought carefully about it, and having scrupulously examined everything, one must then, in conclusion, take as assured that the proposition: *I am, I exist*, is necessarily true, every time I express it or conceive of it in my mind.
>
> (Descartes, 1968, p. 103)

What Descartes concluded, then, was that if he could think about and doubt things he must therefore exist. You may have heard his well-known phrase 'I think therefore I am'. For Descartes, human beings have minds and they have bodies, but they are quite separate from one another. Minds distinguish human beings from all other living creatures, giving them the capacity to think, to speak, to be self-conscious, and to be capable of reflecting on their own nature and the nature of existence (Cohn, 2002).

Cartesian thinking, as Descartes' ideas are called, has been hugely influential. It has been a fundamental building block of modern science. *Thinking* is elevated above *doing* as a higher level activity: thinkers are better rewarded than doers in our society in terms of wealth and status. The rest of the material world, the rest of nature, is there for people to exploit. Knowledge of Cartesian thinking gives an insight into why mental distress is feared more than physical ill health: if we lose our minds, we lose what makes us human. While we can measure physical ill health, by taking temperatures or measuring blood pressure, for instance, the mind is beyond this type of measurement. This, of course, tells us nothing about the nature of the mind–body relationship. Descartes' argument enables you to conclude only that a thinking mind exists, not that a body exists.

Mind–body dualism is one of the central assumptions of the biomedical model. It assumes that there is:

> a clear dichotomy between the mind and the body; physical diseases are presumed to be located solely within the body. As a result, biomedicine tries to understand and treat the body in isolation from other aspects of the person inhabiting it.
>
> (Freund and McGuire, 1995, p. 6)

Dualism helps to explain why some ME sufferers are so keen to distance themselves from psychological causes. Dualism requires that the two components are kept separate, and medical treatments on the whole follow the same assumption. Dualism, however, could be seen as incompatible with the holistic approach which underpins this course.

4.2 Materialism

An alternative view to Cartesian dualism is that mental states are identical to states of the brain. In *materialism* there is no distinction to be made between mind and brain or body. Investigating someone's mind is the same as investigating someone's brain. It is this belief to which Paul Broks's quotation earlier in the unit relates. If you poke about in the brain you find nothing that can be called a self, a consciousness, a mind. He returns to this theme throughout his book, *Into the Silent Land*:

> Like the surface of the Earth, the brain is pretty much mapped. There are no secret compartments inaccessible to the surgeon's knife or the magnetic gaze of the brain scanner; no mysterious humours pervading the cerebral ventricles, no soul in the pineal gland, no vital spark, no spirits in the tangled wood. There is nothing you can't touch or squeeze, weigh or measure, as we might the physical properties of other objects. So you will search in vain for any semblance of a self within the structures of the brain: there is no ghost in the machine. It is time to grow up and accept this fact.
>
> (Broks, 2003, pp. 55–6)

Neurologists are unequivocal in their view that you are never going to capture a mind in someone's body, however hard you hunt. It may be as elusive as the schizophrenia gene or the depression gene. Materialist thinking underpins biological approaches to mental health and distress. The optimistic notion that solutions to mental distress can be found in physiology or biology, such as in genetics or brain chemistry, is founded on a materialist view of the world. And the use of drugs to treat or control mental distress is similarly informed by materialism – if you cannot find the mind, you certainly cannot treat it with pharmacological substances, but you can find pathways in the brain to treat.

4.3 Interactionism or human experience

There is no agreement about which of the above views of the mind–body relationship is to be favoured. There are problems with both: dualism, the view that there is no connection between mind and body, seems contradicted by experiences such as Tessa's account of ME; the view that mind and brain are identical leaves many huge questions unanswered, such as: What creates the emotions? Where is the soul? What is the self?, and so on.

A third view points to the interconnectedness of mind and body and is more in keeping with the course's holistic philosophy. You first came across Seedhouse in Unit 2, where you considered his views on holism, and wholes and parts. He also writes of a *human experience* view, and cites the following:

> Any discussion of mind–body interventions brings the old questions back to life: What are mind and consciousness? How and where do they originate? How are they related to the physical body? In approaching the field of mind–body interventions, it is important that the mind not be viewed as if it were dualistically isolated from the body, as if it were doing something to the body. Mind-body relations are always mutual and bidirectional – the body affects the mind and is affected by it. Mind and body are so integrally related that, in practice, it makes little sense to refer to therapies as solely 'mental' or 'physical. [...] Rather, 'mind–body' could perhaps best be regarded as an overall process that is not easily dissected into separate and distinct components or parts.
>
> (Seedhouse, 2002, p. 55)

This human experience view also accords with a view called *interactionism*, described by Hospers (1990) as:

> the theory that mental and physical events mutually influence one another. Physical events affect mental events: Food poisoning can give you sensations of extreme pain; sirens blowing cause you to feel distress or pain; you receive good news in a letter and feel joy. Mental events also affect the physical: You feel anxious or afraid and your heart beats faster; you decide to take a short walk, and your body begins to move, responding to your decision; you have a 'positive attitude' and this helps you to work efficiently and hold your head high. A thousand daily events in your life and everyone else's seem to confirm the interaction – in fact the mutual dependence – of physical states and states of consciousness.
>
> (Hospers, 1990, p. 254)

Seedhouse (2002) goes on to say:

> The point is that we tie ourselves up by thinking of mind and body as separate – this separation is an artefact which we have excessively institutionalised. We must instead consider *the human experience*, and if we want to promote health we must consider how best we can improve this human experience in general.
>
> (Seedhouse, 2002, p. 59)

In holistic practice, then, it is important not to treat either the body or the mind but both, and to include the other dimensions of the person.

The next activity enables you to consider some views about the mind–body relationship and to reflect on its connection with the holistic perspective that underpins this course.

Activity 5.3 **Make up your ... brain?**

20 minutes Learning outcome 1

Ask two or three people you know well how they would define 'mind' and 'brain' and what they think the relationship between them is. Make some notes on their views.

Then compare their thoughts with the three views of the mind–body relationship you have explored in this section. Which view is closest to the opinion of each person you asked?

Comment Two course testers began with the sort of wordplay in the activity title, thinking about how we use the word 'mind' in common phrases, such as 'make up my mind' and 'out of my mind'. Eventually, they settled on rather similar definitions:

Person 1 brain – the physical organ
mind – the thinking/feeling capacity

Person 2 brain – the physical bit
mind – what you do with your brain.

The scientist Susan Greenfield agrees that there is more to the mind than merely the brain:

> Why else would we need two separate terms? Somehow 'make up your brain', 'narrow-brained' or 'I don't brain' do not have the same ring as the originals. And yet in such phrases, the essence that 'mind' encapsulates is surely the *personal* element.
>
> (Greenfield, 1999, p. xxvii)

5 Mind, body and brain: looking at brain injury

One way we can study the brain is to look at what happens when it is injured. Tessa's brain was not injured: as with many instances of mental distress, her experiences came out of a physically undamaged brain. But damage to the brain gives you another angle from which to reflect on mind–body interactions.

Phineas Gage

Phineas Gage was a 'most efficient and capable man', a foreman in charge of railroad construction in Vermont, USA, in 1848. A tamping iron, over 90 cm in length and about 1 cm diameter, accidentally went through the front of his brain. Amazingly, he made a full physical recovery. He could work, speak and calculate. But his doctor reported him to be:

> fitful, irreverent, indulging at times in the grossest profanity which was not previously his custom, manifesting but little deference for his fellows, impatient of restraint or advice when it conflicts with his desires, at times pertinaciously obstinate, yet capricious and vacillating, devising many plans of future operation which are no sooner arranged than they are abandoned.
>
> (Damasio, 1994, p. 10, quoted in Seedhouse, 2002, p. 50)

Gage's case shows that it is not just intellect that governs our actions. The parts of the brain that had been irreversibly damaged were those that governed his social and emotional capabilities.

That was the view of Phineas Gage's doctor. What about the views of someone who has experienced brain injury? The next activity asks you to read an account of a woman who experienced a serious brain injury but has now substantially recovered.

Activity 5.4 **Brain and mind**

30 minutes

Learning outcome 3

Read Kato's story (Reading 7) in the Resource File. Consider what it tells you about the relationship between the mind and the brain.

Comment

Kato says quite clearly that her mind is her emotions and her personality, and that it worked to protect her from knowledge of the consequences of her brain injury until she was sufficiently recovered to cope with it. This took a long time – at least two years.

She also notes some very direct impacts on her body. There was an immediate loss of control of bodily functions, memory, and speech, and poor balance and co-ordination for some time afterwards. These are impacts that can be fully understood as physical phenomena. The parts of the brain that controlled these functions had been injured, and the worst injury was to the cerebellum, the part of the brain that controls co-ordination, hence the long-lasting damage to that part.

But there are more intangible aspects, which she attributes to her mind:

> I guess this self-absorption was my mind responding to my very traumatised physiological organs, brain and body. My mind was controlling my existence with an awareness that I needed to focus on physically repairing myself.

Kato was not in control of what she thinks of as her mind, but she believes that nonetheless it was acting to protect her. This is similar to Tessa's view that until she was well enough to handle her emotions, her brain and body conspired to keep her from knowing about and facing up to her underlying emotional confusion.

Kato also speculates on what it is to have a mind. She considers whether babies have minds, or whether minds are the product of social interaction.

Finally, the injury appears to have affected her values. She has embarked on a profession which will enable her to care for others whose minds are, for whatever reason, in disarray.

Kato's account is an interesting contrast to Tessa's story. Kato's problems clearly have a physical cause – the car accident – but the impact was on her whole being, her brain, body and mind. Brain or head injuries are less controversial than ME. It is difficult to deny they exist. What might a professional response to Kato's story be? Art therapist Sally Weston, who has considerable experience of working with people who have brain injuries, comments:

> I work as an art therapist offering psychotherapeutic help to people in the early stages (up to about the first 18 months) of recovery from serious brain injury. I work in an NHS neurological rehabilitation unit and I don't often see people years after the event when they have had a chance to make some sense of it all. More people are surviving serious brain injury than ever before, mostly owing to advances in surgical, paramedic and intensive care. Rehabilitation has also developed and many people make a good physical recovery. However, lasting difficulties and changes to previous lifestyle are almost universal. Acquired serious brain injury therefore often incorporates hidden losses and hidden disability.
>
> Since the 1980s patients' psychological needs have begun to be better recognised. According to a survey of relatives of head-injured people, the most difficult enduring problems are personality changes, slowness, poor memory, rapid mood swings, tiredness, depression, irritability, anxiety and threats of violence.
>
> But there are particular issues because it is the brain (or mind) – exactly what someone needs in order to cope with trauma or change – that is damaged. So the person's 'usual' reactions and coping mechanisms may be altered or seem completely changed (for example, memory, learning skills, and the ability to think or organise thoughts). People's ability to monitor their social interactions and emotional control may also be affected.
>
> On the other hand, often the brain/mind/person's ability to heal, and/or find compensation for what has been lost, is amazing. And it can be a real tribute to the power of body, mind and spirit. My clinical experience concurs with Kato's. It is often a privilege to see how individuals cope with devastating injury or disability. The value of peer support and of witnessing others who have experienced a similar event cannot be underestimated.
>
> Both people with brain injury and their relatives benefit from specialist – albeit multidisciplinary – help. I'm part of a multidisciplinary team in which the different professions work closely together. Between us we take care of mind and body – ranging from doctors and physiotherapists to speech and language specialists and

art and music therapies. Art therapy and other psychotherapeutic help are a small, but important and growing, form of help and take account of the importance of the emotions in healing.

So, injury to the brain impacts on the body, emotions, memory and mind. This is evident from an examination of head injury conditions. Yet an understanding of mind and body requires you to draw on a very wide range of disciplines. You may not have expected, when you started this course on mental health, to be considering philosophy. However, you have done so, albeit briefly, in encountering Descartes. Boundaries between disciplines and approaches are strong, and box things into specialisms, such as psychology, medicine, biology, philosophy, so that taking a holistic approach is challenging. This is not a biology course, but in order to understand mind–body links it is useful to know something about the brain. Kato had to relearn many everyday tasks, so the next activity emphasises the importance of the brain in learning.

Activity 5.5 **The brain**

30 minutes

Learning outcome 3

Go to the course K272 website. Using ROUTES, go to the BBC's website about the brain. There you will find a very simplified diagram of the brain. Make brief notes on the functions of the different parts of the brain as described there. Then consider what this information can add to an understanding of the mind–body connections you have been exploring in this unit.

Comment

Some course testers noted that each hemisphere of the brain controls one side of the body. One remembered his grandmother being affected by a brain haemorrhage (which he knew as a 'stroke') on the right side of her body and thought that it must have taken place on the left side of her brain.

Understanding the functions of each part is helpful in understanding the implications of damage to specific parts of the brain. So if the frontal lobes are affected it is possible there will be significant change in personality; if the parietal lobes are damaged the sense of touch may be compromised; if the occipital lobes sustain injury vision may be affected, and if the temporal lobes are harmed memory and language skills may be altered. However, there is a lot about the mind, body and brain relationship which is not explained by understanding the functions of different parts of the brain. This is particularly so in relation to the experience of mental distress and, for example, the impact of medication such as antipsychotics or antidepressants on the brain.

Despite the trauma and long-term damage that head injury wreaks, there is no question that much is understood about it as a condition. Within reason, predictions can be made about the outcome, and people who are affected do have the capacity to learn and relearn. Nevertheless, how different individuals respond cannot be predicted with any certainty. Some rise to the occasion and, like Kato, show a determination to re-engage with life. Others do not. Professionals, who by the nature of things see people mainly in the acute phase, do not necessarily appreciate the extent to which recovery is sustained by intangibles such as character, determination, support from friends and family, or perhaps even chance.

The difficulty of predicting who will succumb to psychological distress, and of explaining why they do, is underlined in the next section, where you look at stress.

6 The experience of stress

Mohan, in one of the stories in Activity 5.1, was described as working very hard and having a range of physical symptoms. His family reported that he smoked and drank excessively. It is possible, although you are not given enough information to be sure, that Mohan is experiencing stress. In this section you explore the nature of stress and consider the connection between mind and body in relation to this common experience. There is a little more biology in this section, this time looking at the way the body reacts to stressors. The next activity asks you to find out more about stress.

Activity 5.6 **Mind, body and the experience of stress**

30 minutes

Learning outcome 3

Go to the K272 course website. Using ROUTES, go to the NHS Direct Online website and search for 'stress'. Make notes in response to the following:

- What is stress?
- What are the symptoms of stress?
- Is stress always negative?
- What happens in the body when someone is 'stressed'?

Comment

No detailed comment is offered here, as the activity requires simple note taking only. However, you may have noticed that both physical and emotional symptoms are listed – a recognition that stress is a disorder of both the body and the mind.

Freund and McGuire (1995, p. 79) point out that stressors can:

> energise and challenge. Stress itself is not inherently unhealthy. It is a part of life, and a totally stressless environment would be both impossible and boring.

Stress affects both mind and body. Mind and body are inextricably linked. As Seedhouse (2002, p. 55) says: 'it isn't my mind and my body that are stressed – I am stressed.'

Stress affects the body in a variety of ways. You will probably be familiar with the 'fight-or-flight' response, which is also referred to as the stress response. When you are threatened or frightened in some way, your body's response is to get ready to react by either fighting or fleeing. Physiologically, the response is caused by the nervous system (which includes the brain and spinal cord) and the release of certain hormones. Hormones are the body's chemical messengers. They are released by the endocrine glands and depress or stimulate functions of the body. Adrenaline (or epinephrine) and noradrenalin (or norepinephrine) are examples of stress hormones known as catecholamines. A number of things happen as the body adapts for fight or flight:

- The blood pressure is raised. Blood is diverted from the outer parts of the body (which is why the hands and feet may be cold at times of stress) to the muscles and heart.
- Fats (including cholesterol) and sugars are released to give the body energy.
- Immunity is temporarily depressed, which allows the body to get ready for possible invasions, such as wounds.

Such bodily changes may cause physical problems. So, for example, ongoing stress might contribute to heart disease owing to the release of fats and sugars into the body. However, people react to, and deal with, stress in different ways. Three interrelated responses are:

- physiological reactivity (the ways bodies react to stress)
- cognitive–emotional appraisal (the way people perceive and assess stressors)
- coping (the way people respond to or manage stress).

You now look at each of these in turn.

Physiological reactivity

Two people experiencing the same stressor may respond differently in the way their blood pressure changes as their bodies shift from being in a state of fight or flight to one of relaxation. Gender differences have been suggested in relation to the amount of stress hormones produced, with men producing more than women (Freund and McGuire, 1995). It is uncertain why there are physiological differences between people. It is suggested that there may be genetic predispositions to, for example, hypertension and coronary heart disease and also that social factors may have a part to play (Freund and McGuire, 1995). Physiological responses may be influenced by the way men and women are socialised to respond to stress, and long-term exposure to stress may lead to learned responses which in turn modify physiological responses. It is concluded that the relationship between physiological factors and social factors is not clear-cut.

Cognitive–emotional appraisal

Cognitive–emotional appraisal relates to how people interpret and react to a stressful event. It has been suggested that those with a high ‘sense of coherence’ are healthier, this being defined as ‘dispositional orientation toward experiencing stressors as comprehensible, manageable and meaningful’ (Antonovsky, 1990, cited by Freund and McGuire, 1995, p. 83). It seems, then, that if you are able to understand and feel that you are capable of overcoming and finding meaning in the stressors you encounter, you will be better able to manage them. It has also been suggested that cultural factors and position in the social structure can affect people’s sense of coherence. Freund and McGuire point to the significance of people feeling a sense of empowerment and control, and of their past experiences. They say: ‘A lifetime of social exploitation or domination will certainly have an impact on whether a person feels empowered’ (1995, p. 84).

Coping

Individual differences are also identified in the ways people manage the tension produced by a stressor. Freund and McGuire (1995, p. 84) point out that:

> One’s cognitive–emotional appraisal of a situation is in itself a way of coping or managing stress. Some people ‘overact’ emotionally; seeing the glass as half-empty, they give up. Others see a glass that is half-full and keep striving. Coping is not merely a matter of attitude, perception, or emotional response, however; it also involves action – that is, doing something about the stressor.

In other words, for some reason some people have an attitude which helps them manage stress better than others. You might speculate that the amount of support available can also act as a buffer against stress, as can having enough money to buy help in some circumstances. This is what the holistic model would suggest.

As you can see, in relation to stress there is much interaction between different aspects of the person and between the person and their environment. If Mohan's 'symptoms' are due to stress it becomes clear that responses which target only the biological or psychological aspects of the individual are likely to be inadequate: stress impacts not just on the body or on the mind, but on both. This highlights the importance of a holistic approach which considers the social, emotional and spiritual aspects of the person. It therefore challenges the way services have been set up to compartmentalise specialised responses and treatments. There is every reason to retain specialisms – Kato, for example, was taught to walk again by a very competent physiotherapist – but workers need to remember that there is often a whole raft of causes of mental distress which need to be acknowledged.

7 Conclusion

This unit opened with a long list of questions. You may not have found answers to all of them; indeed, it is debatable whether they can be answered. We hope you have been prompted to think more deeply about them. The relationship between mind and body is of practical as well as academic interest in relation to mental health and distress. ME, brain injury and stress are examples which illustrate the interconnection well.

When people's individual experiences are considered, the close connections between physical and mental states become clear. To some degree services recognise this; for example, the NHS Direct web pages list both physical and mental symptoms of stress. However, many standard treatments seem to assume either a mental or a physical cause and response, separating the two. Holistic approaches, although they may be more challenging in their implications (and far harder to implement), recognise that people are more than physical beings, and attempt to find ways of addressing problems with a mixture of strategies.

References

Antonovsky, A. (1990) 'Personality and health: testing the sense of coherence model' in Friedman, H.S. (ed.) *Personality and Disease*, New York, Wiley, pp. 155–77.

Bell, D. (1995) *The Doctor's Guide to Chronic Fatigue Syndrome*, Boston, Mass., Addison-Wesley.

Blackburn, S. (1999) *Think*, Oxford, Oxford University Press.

Bridges, K. and Goldberg, D.P. (1985) 'Somatic presentations of DSM III psychiatric disorders in primary care', *Psychological Medicine*, Vol. 21, pp. 473–83.

Broks, P. (2003) *Into the Silent Land: Travels in Neuropsychology*, London, Atlantic Books.

Cohn, H. (2002) *Heidegger and the Roots of Existential Therapy*, London, Continuum.

Damasio, A. (1994) *Descartes' Error*, New York, Grosset/Putnam.

Descartes, R. (1968) *Discourse on Method and the Meditations* (first published 1637 and 1641), Harmondsworth, Penguin Classics.

Freund, P.E.S. and McGuire, M.B. (1995) *Health, Illness and the Social Body: A Critical Sociology*, Englewood Cliffs, N.J., Prentice Hall.

Greenfield, S. (1999) 'Making up our minds', *New Statesman*, 27 September, pp. xxviii–xxix.

Harrison, A. (2001) 'Somatisation', *Mental Health Practice*, Vol. 4, No. 6, pp. 31–8.

Hospers, J. (1990) *An Introduction to Philosophical Analysis*, 3rd edition, London, Routledge.

Lipowski, Z.J. (1988) 'Somatization: the concept and its clinical application', *American Journal of Psychiatry*, Vol. 145, pp. 1358–68.

Seedhouse, D. (2002) *Total Health Promotion: Mental Health, Rational Fields and the Quest for Autonomy*, Chichester, Wiley.

Showalter, E. (1997) *Hystories*, London, Picador.

Smith, R.C. (1985) 'A clinical approach to the somatising patient', *Journal of Family Practice*, Vol. 21, pp. 294–301.

Unit 6 Boundaries of Exclusion

Contents

You will need:

Audio 1 'Shifting boundaries'

Learning outcomes

After studying this unit you should be able to:

1 explain the impact of stereotypes, stigma and discrimination on people who experience mental distress

2 discuss the nature and implications of exclusion and inclusion in relation to mental distress

3 understand the implications of citizenship for service users/survivors and workers

4 consider how to promote citizenship and support service user/survivor involvement.

1 Introduction

> To tackle social exclusion not only means changing our views on who is or is not 'employable', or changing our laws on who has a right to live where. It also means changing our conversations in bars – challenging discrimination at the micro, personal, level of how we think and act.
>
> (Sayce, 2000, p. 8)

By keeping a focus on the person as a citizen at the centre of the holistic model, you explore in this unit how the notion of citizenship provides a means to challenge exclusion and increase social inclusion. 'Social inclusion' and 'social exclusion' are phrases that seem to have appeared with increasing regularity in recent times. Some people might argue that they are only the repackaging of poverty, discrimination and inequality; others that the terms are used to focus on paid employment as the only means of ensuring citizenship, but at the expense of state welfare support. One thing is certain, though: however politicians may use the terms, many people who have come into contact with mental health services have experienced the discrimination and stigma that exclusion brings.

Significant implications follow from a psychiatric diagnosis or label: in the ways that family and friends respond to the diagnosis, mental health services respond to people in distress, service users/survivors are portrayed by the media, and people experience access to employment. In this unit you consider the nature of stereotypes, stigma and discrimination in relation to social exclusion. By using the concept of citizenship you then go on to focus on service user/survivor involvement and the opportunities and challenges it presents.

2 Stereotypes, stigma and discrimination

In Unit 4 you read about the significance of ethnic and cultural identities and the dangers of stereotyping, and considered the impacts of racism at individual and institutional levels. You now consider the significance of stigma, stereotypes and discrimination in relation to mental distress and a service user/survivor identity. 'Service user/survivor' may be only one of several identities that someone may have: others may be mother, sister, worker, artist or neighbour, for instance. However, a service user/survivor identity may still have a disproportionate effect on the person's life if others see it as a complete identity, and stereotypes play a key role in this. How do stereotypes arise in relation to mental distress? What does stigma mean in this context?

Stereotypes may seem innocuous and at times even humorous. You may, for example, have smiled at jokes based on 'mother-in-law' or gender stereotypes. Stereotypes can be negative, positive or a mixture. Examples of stereotypes that could be construed as negative are those of the English as 'stiff-upper-lipped' and the Scots as careful with their money. Positive stereotypes relate to certain professions: teachers as caring and conscientious and nurses as 'angels', for example.

The video 'A quiet night on Roundhay Wing', which you watched in Unit 1, uses stereotypes – particularly of mental health professionals and services – to illustrate some very powerful points in a humorous way. In the case of mental distress, the stereotypes seem to fall into two main categories: dangerous and helpless. The dangerous stereotype is most strongly associated with diagnoses of schizophrenia and personality disorder. This is the 'mad, wide-eyed, violent' stereotype which is frequently reinforced by strong media images, ranging from news and current affairs to soap operas and films. On the other hand, the stereotype of helplessness and hopelessness is more strongly associated with a diagnosis of depression, incorporating the image of someone who is unable to take control of their life and who is to be pitied or ridiculed.

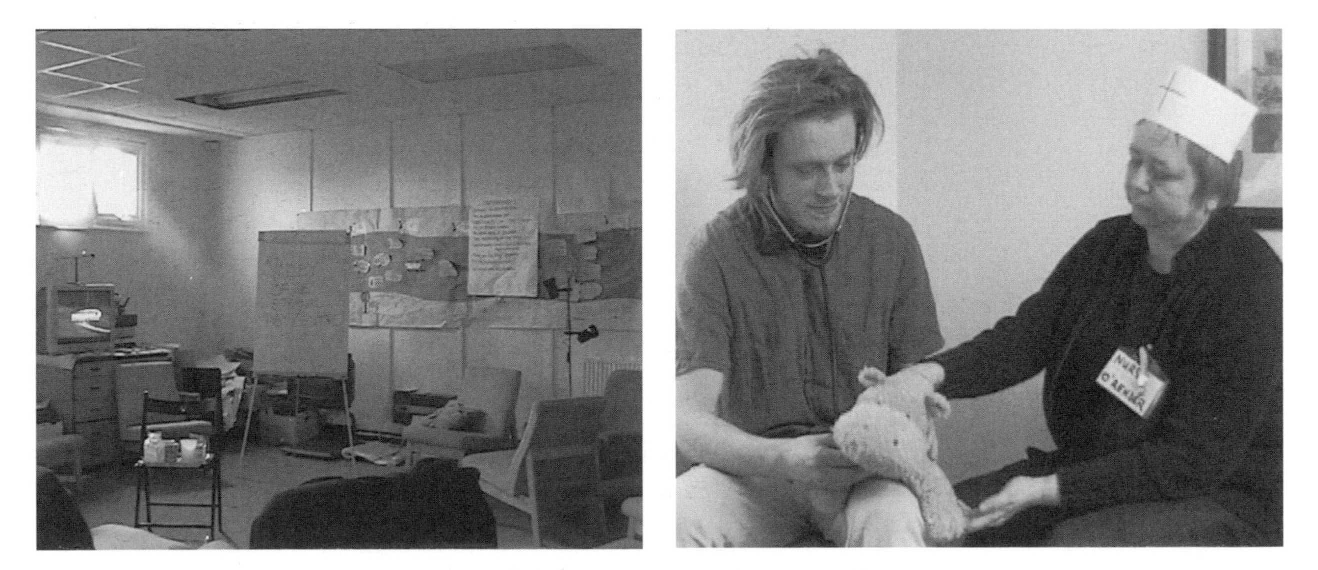

Some diagnoses are stereotyped more negatively than others. For example, it is possible to identify a category of people who experience high levels of anxiety, portrayed in films such as Woody Allen's *Annie Hall*. Moreover, some stereotypes of mental distress can actually be positive: some experiences of mental distress are associated with art and creativity. The examples of Van Gogh, Tchaikovsky and more recently Spike Milligan spring to mind.

Whereas stereotypes do not necessarily have negative implications, the same cannot be said of stigma. Goffman (1990) writes that ancient Greeks used the term to refer to signs that were cut or burnt into the body to advertise that someone was disgraced, polluted and to be avoided. Nowadays, stigma does not necessarily have a physical element, although side effects of some medication may be highly visible. Goffman argues that the term is used more to apply to the disgrace itself rather than any physical evidence of it. To be mentally distressed is to be stigmatised, as Sayce notes:

> People with mental illness are portrayed as morally lacking – shameful, dangerous, irresponsible. A stock of 'ideal types' and narratives flows through both fictional and non-fictional accounts of mental illness: the psycho-killer [...] the pathetic, useless neglected person [...] the person whose craziness is used as a source of humour.
>
> (Sayce, 2000, pp. 60–1)

So whereas stereotypes can be positive, negative or ambivalent and may be used constructively, stigma is firmly negative. It seems, then, that there are links between stigma, stereotypes and the discrimination you encountered in Unit 4. A stereotype is a widely understood form of description for people belonging to a certain group: traffic wardens are often portrayed as inflexible, officious people, for example. But a stereotype ignores diversity within the group: some traffic wardens may not be very pleasant people, but some will be. Just as some nurses may be downright unpleasant, others will be more like the stereotypical 'angel'. What might the practical implications of stigma and stereotypes be?

Activity 6.1 **Understanding stigma**

30 minutes

Learning outcomes 1 and 2

First, spend a few minutes thinking about the following scenario:

> Your life stops for two weeks and then starts again. Nothing has changed, except that you have been given a diagnosis of schizophrenia.

You do not need to know any details about schizophrenia. Concentrate on the stereotypes and assumptions associated with it.

If you have received such a diagnosis, write down what you actually did in response to it and what the implications of the diagnosis were. If you haven't, answer the following questions:

- Who would you tell and why?
- How do you think people would respond in your workplace, in your home life or close relationships, and in your financial affairs?

Comment

Course testers found this activity challenging, especially as some testers held particular stereotypes about schizophrenia themselves. One wrote:

> I imagine it would be very hard to tell friends and family and I might feel some shame. I would consider telling my employer but if the diagnosis became known at work, I think serious questions would be raised about my abilities and I would be seen as unreliable.

Another course tester was concerned at the possible permanency of the diagnosis. She thought that if she told anyone, that would be the first thing the person would think about whenever they met. This course tester was also concerned at how her family had reacted to news items in which schizophrenia was associated with dangerousness, and worried about what her family might think of her.

Sayce (2000) discusses research into common responses of people who are given a psychiatric diagnosis. They include:

Shame: 'I hope no one finds out.'

Terror: 'What will happen to me now?'

Fear of isolation: 'No one will want to know me now.'

Grief: 'My life is over.'

Disbelief: 'It must be a mistake.'

Anger: 'Why me? It's not fair.'

Negative responses to being given a psychiatric diagnosis are likely to be influenced by the stigma that is attached to mental illness. However, the concept of stigma has also been the subject of debate (Sayce, 2000). The label of mental illness suggests there is something wrong with the individual, thus locating the stigma with the individual person and ignoring the way other people perpetuate it by their negative responses, whereas a focus on the impact of discrimination in its wider, social context should include the inappropriate responses of others.

Whether negative stereotyping and stigma come about as a result of misunderstanding mental distress or of the process of diagnosis, there is no doubt that prejudice, discrimination and exclusion can and do follow.

3 Social exclusion

3.1 Describing exclusion

Social exclusion is now much talked about and the links between exclusion and mental distress have received government attention. The Social Exclusion Unit in England is, at the time of writing (March 2004), gathering evidence for a project on mental health and social exclusion. The findings are expected in late 2004. Poppy Buchanan-Barker and Phil Barker (personal communication) have drawn a parallel between experiences of Nazi Germany in the 1930s and today, as the poems below illustrate.

20th Century Values

First they came for the Communists
And I didn't speak up
Because I wasn't a Communist.

Then they came for the Jews
And I didn't speak up
Because I wasn't a Jew.

Then they came for the trade unionists
And I didn't speak up
Because I wasn't a trade unionist.

Then they came for the Catholics
And I didn't speak up
Because I was a Protestant.

Then they came for me –
And by that time
No one was left to speak up.

(Based on the words of Pastor Martin Niemoeller, victim of the Nazis)

21st Century Values

First they came for the dispossessed
But we didn't speak up
Because we thought that we weren't dispossessed.

Then they came for the marginalized
But we didn't speak up –
Because we thought that we weren't marginalized.

Then they came for the dissidents
But we didn't speak up
Because we thought that we weren't dissidents.

Next they came for the asylum seekers
But we didn't speak up –
Because we thought that we would never be asylum seekers.

Then they came for the mentally ill
And there was no one left to speak for anyone.

So do you think exclusion is something new, or is it another name for poverty and all the deprivation that goes with being poor? Poverty usually refers to the lack of material resources for an individual or family, but may also describe whole communities. The concept of social exclusion acknowledges the related issues that stem from poverty, such as an absence of social participation and integration. Thus it is not just about poverty in a financial sense, but includes inequality and the lack of such intangibles as opportunity, access to services and information, experience, and political and social rights. The government's Social Exclusion Unit defines exclusion as:

> a shorthand term for what can happen when people or areas suffer from a combination of linked problems such as unemployment, poor skills, low incomes, poor housing, high crime environments, bad health and family breakdown.
>
> (Social Exclusion Unit, 2001)

Miller (2000) reported on research by Mind into the implications of social exclusion for mental health service users/survivors. These are summarised in Box 6.1.

Box 6.1 Social exclusion

How exclusion operates in daily life, illustrated by witness statements from Mind's inquiry into social exclusion[1]:

- **Social – people become isolated, abused or live in fear**
  Those experiencing social exclusion often have few friends, family or neighbours they can call on for help. They may be physically or sexually abused, harassed outside of the home, or live in fear of being burgled or their children getting involved with drugs or crime. *'Care in the community is experienced as a cordon sanitaire of professionals and service users. Strip those away and the social network of many mental health service users drops to zero.'*
- **Cultural – people are not able to be themselves**
  Social exclusion makes it hard for individuals to get on with their lives, because they are put down or harassed because of their disability, race, religious beliefs, their social customs, language, food and music, or because they are lesbians or gay men. *'Why is it that black people are more likely to be offered drugs than counselling? In Leeds, when a counselling service for black people was opened, demand was extensive.'*
- **Economic – people can't afford a decent standard of living**
  Excluded people often suffer discrimination from financial services. Or they may be unable to afford quality housing, food, clothes, heating and the other things that make up a decent standard of living, because they are in low-paid or casual jobs, unemployed, living on benefit or the basic state pension. *'I am charged a 60 per cent loading on my insurance cover despite a disputed diagnosis.'*
- **Political – people can't get back-up**
  People experiencing exclusion often do not know how to get, or cannot access the help they need from politicians, aren't taken seriously by political parties and service providers, and do not get the backing of powerful pressure groups. *'You're not taken seriously by the police because you have a mental health record.'*

Reference

1 Mind (1999) *Creating Accepting Communities: Report of the Mind Enquiry into Social Exclusion.*

(Source: Miller, 2000, p. 10)

Social contact and support are considered very important by service users/survivors. However, relationships with family and friends and the wider community are not always helpful. A survey called *Pull Yourself Together!* (MHF, 2000) found that over half the people who took part in the research had experienced some form of unfair treatment within their families. A lack of understanding was the most frequently expressed theme, but the findings also included instances of contact being reduced or stopped, people being ostracised from their families, name calling and other hurtful comments, and unhelpful advice, including the cliché that gave the report its name. The survey also found that just over half of service users/survivors had experienced unfair treatment from friends.

Perhaps one of the most striking findings from such research is the amount of unpleasant, frightening and sometimes dangerous behaviour that people with mental health problems have to endure from neighbours. *Give us a Break*, a Scottish survey (NSF Scotland, 2001), explored the harassment of people with mental health problems. It found that 41 per cent had experienced some form of harassment, compared with 15 per cent of the general population. Verbal abuse was the most common. Over half of those surveyed said it referred directly to their mental health problems, while others experienced damage to their property and some had been physically attacked; nearly one in three of those experiencing harassment had had to move house to escape it.

> They were calling me names such as 'loony' and saying 'you should be locked up'.
>
> They set fire to my front door, broke my windows and called me names.
>
> We passed two local lads and they started throwing stones at me and shouting and laughing. The stones cut my ear and hurt my cheek.
>
> (NSF Scotland, 2001, p. 7)

Another way in which people are made to feel unwelcome and excluded is when local communities organise NIMBY ('not in my back yard') campaigns to stop facilities such as day centres or supported housing being set up in their neighbourhoods. Sayce (2000) reports a survey that found two-thirds of local Mind associations had encountered opposition to mental health facilities in the previous five years. This included protest letters, meetings and violence directed at service users/survivors, staff and property.

Even if people are met with welcoming and supportive communities, the financial implications of contact with mental health services can drastically affect people's incomes, whether or not they are employed. For example, state benefits will be reduced after a period in hospital, including housing benefit, which in turn may affect someone's tenancy or mortgage. Someone who returns to work will no longer be eligible for some state benefits, but if they then find they are not able to continue working they may not be eligible for the benefits they were entitled to previously. Mind's illustration of the 'benefits game' overleaf illustrates the process.

One possible way into work is through supported employment schemes. These are sheltered work schemes in which people do a range of tasks as if they were in employment. For example, some schemes have strict starting and finishing times, intended to mirror the working day. Schemes are only able to pay a limited amount, called 'therapeutic earnings', otherwise people employed on them will inevitably lose benefits. At the time of writing (March 2004) this means that in some cases people are working for a full week or more for around £20.

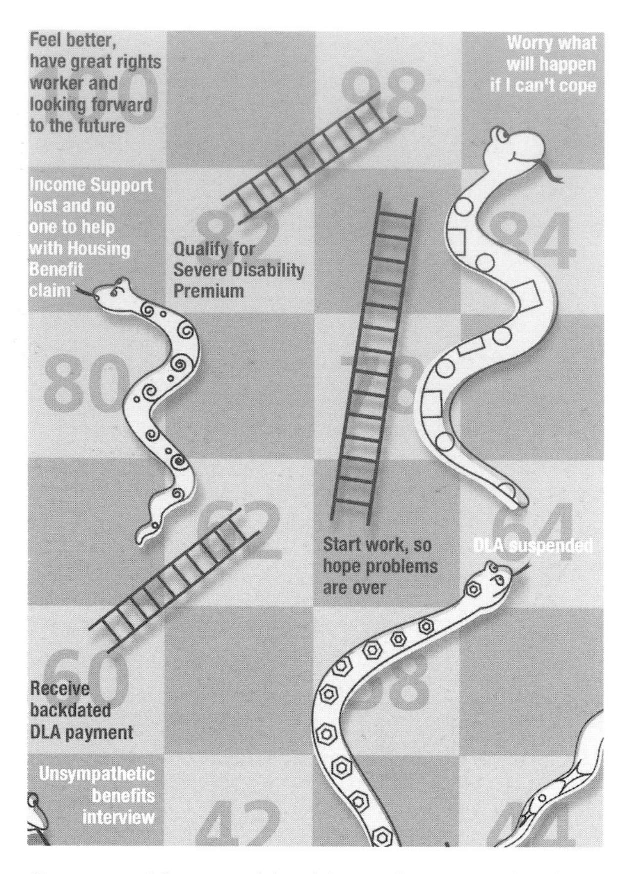

Contact with mental health services can also have a detrimental effect on people's job prospects. A survey of disabled people (ONS, 1999) found that people giving mental health problems as their main disability are more likely to be unemployed than people with any other category of disability. Fewer than one in five (19 per cent) were employed. This low figure can be partly explained by the obstacles faced by people who have (or have previously had) a diagnosis of mental illness when they apply for work. They are exemplified by this account from a report from a Mind survey:

> On two occasions I lied when I applied for jobs. On both these occasions I said that my two and a half year absence from employment was due to a term spent in prison. I was accepted for the first and short listed for the second. Whenever I have been truthful about my psychiatric past, I have never been accepted for a job.
>
> (Read and Baker, 1996, p. 9)

This Mind survey found that a third of the people responding thought they had been unfairly dismissed or forced to resign from their jobs. With such levels of prejudice and discrimination, service users/survivors may encounter problems in assuming an identity as a worker. Despite the challenges, however, there is some positive evidence that service users/survivors can and do successfully progress from a service user identity to that of employee.

However, it cannot be assumed that just because some people who experience mental distress feel they benefit from a worker identity, everyone will. Some service users/survivors argue that there are ways other than paid employment to make a valuable contribution to society (Kay Sheldon, personal communication): through voluntary work, service user involvement and education, for example.

3.2 Feeling excluded

Various forms of exclusion are experienced by many people on a daily basis. You now explore the impacts of exclusion and what they may *feel* like. The next activity may raise strong feelings, so please bear that in mind as you plan your work.

Activity 6.2 **Experiences of exclusion**

30 minutes

Learning outcome 2

Exclusion is not a one-way transaction, nor is it necessarily visible. For someone to be excluded, someone else, or a group or an institution, must do the excluding. Write a couple of paragraphs – as if for a journal or diary entry – about an occasion when you felt excluded and then about an occasion when you think you may have excluded someone else. Try to describe your emotions during and after both incidents.

Comment

Course testers remembered being excluded as children and as adults. Remembering not being invited to a party at the age of nine, a tester commented:

> It seemed like I was the only person in the class who didn't get an invite and it left me feeling very lonely.

To have such a strong memory so many years later gives an indication of the lasting impact of exclusion. Another course tester wrote about how he eventually left his job because of consistent exclusion:

> The effect of this left me feeling devalued, that my efforts were for nothing, and I was unable to continue in my present role. I saw this very much as personal rejection. Those I had covered for, and supported, no longer appeared to want to acknowledge me.

Course testers found thinking about ways they had excluded other people challenging but ultimately helpful, because it brought the concept of exclusion into their own experiences.

In this activity you were asked to think about specific instances and your reactions to them. However, social exclusion is more than one-off incidents and events. It can also be an enduring, debilitating and seemingly hopeless situation.

Up to now your focus has been on exclusion – not surprising in a unit with exclusion in the title! But how can social exclusion be challenged? What counts as social inclusion? Is it an impossible dream? In the rest of this unit you look at working towards inclusion and at how concepts of citizenship might be used to help tackle exclusion and discrimination.

4 Inclusion

Social inclusion has been identified as a key priority for mental health policy and practice (Sainsbury Centre, 2002). A number of initiatives have combined to support this:

- Legislation. The implementation of the Disability Discrimination Act 1995 and the Human Rights Act 1998 emphasises the need for inclusion. The Health Act 1999 and the Welfare to Work strategy (DSS, 1998) emphasise inter-agency collaboration and partnership.
- The National Service Framework (NSF) for Mental Health (DH, 1999). Standard One relates to mental health promotion, and social inclusion is more likely to promote mental health.
- The recovery movement, which emphasises autonomy and empowerment (Unit 21 considers debates about recovery).
- Community development and democratic renewal work. This aims to create 'active' and welcoming communities, including reaching out to those who have experienced mental distress.
- The user movement more broadly. There is 'strong evidence', according to the Sainsbury Centre (2002), that social inclusion is desired and can make a positive impact on mental wellbeing.

Miller (2000) argues that as well as debates about social exclusion, debates about citizenship and rights need to take place so that people who experience mental distress are not excluded socially, culturally, economically or politically. There are some signs of positive developments in the UK in this respect: there is now legislation which relates specifically to discrimination and disability, and also human rights legislation.

The Sainsbury Centre suggests three approaches to social inclusion:

- Inclusion as access: do mental health service users/survivors have full access to services, information, decision making and jobs?
- Inclusion as a standard of living: what, for example, is being done to ensure that people have a good standard of health, and opportunities to learn skills, to work, to earn a wage and to live safely?
- Inclusion as relationships: this emphasises equality and mutual respect, and promoting ways of developing friendships.

In her discussion of an 'inclusion model' Sayce (2000) writes of the importance of working with other disability groups, having disability rights slogans which are 'mental health friendly', and creating alliances with other excluded groups such as young people leaving care and asylum seekers. How easy do you think that would be? These groups are as likely to hold negative stereotypes about people experiencing mental health difficulties as the rest of the community, and so partnerships may take some time to develop. Sayce recommends taking positive steps to show employers and colleges, for example, that service users/ survivors can work and study, although she cautions against making issues more simplistic than they are:

> To dismantle discrimination, one has to complexify issues. Most people have multiple identities: a woman user/survivor of Irish descent, a deaf person diagnosed with schizophrenia. Unpicking the interwoven stereotypes, understanding the way in which barriers compound each other, is central to inclusion work. Solutions, too, must be complex. It is no help to reduce employers' preconceptions if social security disincentives make work non-viable

> or if treatment regimes are premised on the notion that user/survivors will not work and that adverse drug effects such as thinking slowly or shuffling are therefore tolerable.
>
> (Sayce, 2000, p. 246)

One of the driving forces towards inclusion identified above is legislation. Two of the most significant recent pieces of legislation with the potential to promote social inclusion are the Human Rights Act (HRA) 1998 and the Disability Discrimination Act (DDA) 1995. The implementation of the HRA 1998 in 2000 effectively enshrined the European Convention on Human Rights in UK law and this has been viewed positively in relation to mental health service users'/survivors' experiences. The National Service Framework (DH, 1999) applies to all people in the mental health care system, not only those detained under the Mental Health Act. You will explore the impact of human rights legislation on mental health services in more detail in Unit 22.

Thus everyone has rights under legislation and rights as a citizen. However, people's rights may be compromised if they have a mental health service user/survivor identity or role, and they are likely to experience discrimination. Sayce argues that emphasising citizenship is key to promoting inclusion:

> The aim [of a 'disability inclusion model'] is citizenship inclusion, on a fair basis with all other citizens – and fairness for would-be citizens, who should not be barred from immigration on the grounds of mental disorder. This would change user/survivors' lived experience – people's income, opportunities and legal rights – [...] making it easier for people to seek help. The paternalistic notion that all disabled people need is 'services' to 'help' them has to be replaced by a broader view of people's aspirations and potential.
>
> (Sayce, 2000, p. 129)

But what does citizenship mean? How does the identity or role of citizen differ from that of service user/survivor? In the next section you consider the relationship between citizenship and mental distress.

5 Citizenship

5.1 Active and passive citizenship

In a paper presented to a seminar at the Centre for Citizenship and Community Mental Health at the University of Bradford, Pat Bracken talked about what he understands by the term 'citizen':

> someone who is allowed to, and feels able to, participate fully in the society of which he/she is a member; someone who benefits from the rights and carries the responsibilities available to other members of that society. The citizen only forfeits his/her rights if he/she contravenes the laws of that society. However, the level of responsibility expected of any individual varies throughout the life-cycle and particularly in relation to episodes of illness.
>
> I also use the term to indicate something beyond these legalistic connotations. Our analysis is close to that of the writer Michael Ignatieff who says that:
>
> > 'Citizenship has its active modes (running for political office, voting, political organizing) and its passive modes (entitlement to rights and welfare).'
> >
> > (Ignatieff, 1989, p. 63)
>
> Ignatieff makes the point that both these modes of citizenship go together and cannot be separated.
>
> (Bracken, 2003, pp. 1–2)

Bracken's summary of the idea of active and passive citizenship is:

- Passive citizenship:
  - Freedom from oppression and discrimination
  - Entitlement to benefits and support
- Active citizenship:
  - Freedom to define one's own identity
  - Being able to celebrate one's identity

Bracken goes on to propose that citizenship can be the vehicle that brings together useful elements of all the various explanatory models in mental health. This seems to suggest that it can cross boundaries between models, and so can be an integrating force – hence the idea of the person as citizen at the centre of the holistic model that underpins the course.

The rights and responsibilities of citizenship are inextricably linked. Bracken (2003) argues that involvement in mental health services is often accompanied by a loss of citizenship. If mental health professionals could work towards thinking and responding outside the narrow confines of specific professional models, the challenges posed by adopting a model of citizenship could be met.

One way to understand citizenship is to think about what losing it might be like. In the next activity you will listen to Bracken talking about loss of citizenship.

Activity 6.3 **Citizen rules, OK**

1 hour

Learning outcome 4

Listen to the interview with Pat Bracken on Audio 1, track 4 and make some notes on what he sees as the impact and challenges of the concept of citizenship in mental health.

Comment

A course tester who has used mental health services and works in the voluntary sector commented:

> Bracken argues that as well as distress caused by symptoms, people experience great difficulties as a result of loss of citizenship. Loss of citizenship comes along with the diagnosis and includes loss of social position, employment, housing, relationships and all aspects of social access. It's difficult to separate distress from social context. People are connected and interrelated in a social world. This fits with the holistic model and the person at the centre as a citizen, but also with the wider holistic perspective of people within groups, communities and environments.
>
> Bracken thinks that mental health work should be aimed at establishing the citizenship of people experiencing mental health difficulties. Sometimes the diagnosis comes as a relief to some people; however, it may also serve to take service users/survivors away from what is actually happening in their lives.
>
> Citizenship reframes problems away from an individual, medical focus. This might present a challenge to service users/survivors because they will need to take more responsibility for what is happening to them.
>
> People are beginning to want a different kind of relationship with doctors and psychiatrists – a kind of active citizenship. Bracken suggests that professionals start to be critical of their own practice. Change is possible, and Bracken uses the example of homosexuality and the Gay Pride movement to illustrate how practice can change.
>
> A challenge Bracken identifies is that of compulsion and maintaining citizenship rights when compulsion is framed in medical terms.

Not being a full citizen of one's society means that essentially one has 'a life less worthy' than others' (Figure 6.1). The implications of this are extremely serious and pervasive, and Bracken argues that no list of the effects of loss of citizenship will ever be complete.

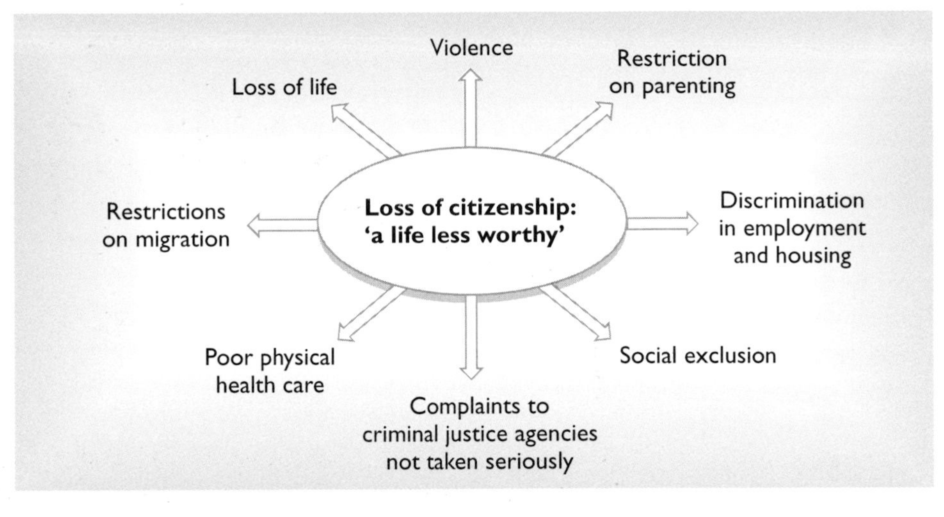

Figure 6.1 Loss of citizenship (Source: Bracken, 2003)

Bracken describes these effects in detail as follows:

> **Loss of life**: inmates of mental hospitals were sent to the gas chambers by the Nazis alongside others who became 'non-citizens' such as Jewish people and homosexuals. At least 250,000 people with mental or physical impairments were killed in this way (United States Holocaust Memorial Museum, 1996).
>
> **Violence**: being regarded as 'mentally ill' can lead to violence and physical abuse. Read and Baker (1996) found that of 778 service-users who responded to a survey 47% said that they had been physically attacked at some point [...]
>
> **Restriction on parenting rights**: this ranges from forced sterilisation programmes to unwarranted questioning of parental skills. The former took place in the US and in a number of European countries (Sweden, Norway, Denmark, Finland, Estonia and Germany) in the first half of the 20th century in an effort to reduce the number of 'feeble minded' in society (Lombardo, 1983; Sayce, 2000). [...] Mental health service users can make good, bad or indifferent parents. There is no consistent or convincing body of evidence that people with a mental illness diagnosis are necessarily poor parents (Mowbray *et al.*, 1995). In spite of this, parents with a psychiatric diagnosis lose custody for reasons that would rarely lead to the same outcome with 'normal' parents such as 'bad attitude or sexual promiscuity' (Stefan, 1989).
>
> **Restriction on migration**: a history of 'mental disorder' in itself can debar an individual from entry to the US. Liz Sayce quotes from the visa waiver forms that entrants to the US are given. The entrant is asked if any of the following apply to him/her: 'moral turpitude, prior engagement in espionage, terrorist activities, genocide – or mental disorder' (Sayce, 2000, p. 56).
>
> **Discrimination and exclusion in different areas of social and economic life**: there is evidence that people with a history of 'serious mental illness' move down the social ladder and often end up living in poverty (Pilgrim and Rogers, 1999). This is usually understood in terms of the 'social drift' hypothesis according to which 'schizophrenia', in itself, undermines the individual's ability to work productively. However, there is also evidence that poverty, social exclusion and isolation result from discrimination in areas such as employment (Read and Baker, 1996) and housing (Page, 1977).

Huxley and Thornicroft (2003) point out that in the UK in recent years 'the employment level of psychiatric patient populations rarely reaches more than 10% and when working they work fewer hours and earn only two-thirds of the national average hourly rate' (p. 289).

Poor physical health care: standardised mortality rates for people with a history of mental illness are much higher than the population average. Medical personnel sometimes do not take the medical complaints of mental health service users seriously. As a result diagnosis of cancer and other serious illnesses can be delayed (Sayce and Measey, 1999).

Complaints to criminal justice agencies not taken seriously: having a history of mental health problems or psychiatric service involvement can mean that complaints to the police and other agencies are not taken as seriously as they warrant. Individuals in this situation may be thought of as being an 'unreliable witness' (Home Office, 1998). There is mounting evidence that rape has been commonplace in psychiatric hospitals and yet few prosecutions have been successful.

Exclusion from society: some politicians and organisations continue to campaign for the social exclusion of people with mental health problems. Thus we heard from the last UK Minister of Health that 'care in the community has failed'. The implications of this statement are extremely serious; essentially it is an assertion that such individuals have no right to be 'in the community'. One study found that two-thirds of mental health service providers surveyed (both statutory and voluntary sector) had experienced 'nimby' ('not in my backyard') opposition to planned service changes between 1992 and 1997 (Repper *et al.*, 1997).

(Bracken, 2003, pp. 2–4)

Activity 6.4 **Excluding citizenship**

30 minutes Learning outcomes 2 and 4

Rufus May has direct experience of some of the effects Bracken identifies. Listen to his interview on track 5 of Audio 1 and make some notes on the challenges that have faced him in his life and profession, and to some extent still do.

Comment

One course tester who works in mental health commented:

> The challenge of coping with living a lie is very powerful and something I can identify with. Trust is a big issue and I am wary of telling my story and sharing my experiences with the 'wrong' person, especially colleagues. If people are not taken seriously as service users, will they be taken seriously as workers in the same field? May talked about 'personal wisdom', but where does this fit with professional cultures that reflect stereotypes, prejudice and stigma?

However, although May has had some very distressing experiences, he is optimistic and talks of the importance of having a holistic approach and of crossing boundaries between professions and ways of working.

Up to now you have looked at active and passive citizenship and the challenges that the loss of citizenship poses, but what can be done to promote citizenship? Employment has a central role in discussions about citizenship and inclusion, and it is to this that you now turn.

5.2 Employment

There are many challenges encountered by people whose identity is affected by their mental health experiences when they look for or return to employment, such as discrimination and a lack of support. Some employers are now taking seriously the positive contribution that service users/survivors can make to their organisations. An example of the impact of an innovative programme is described in Box 6.2.

Box 6.2

Between 1995 and 2002 the User Employment Programme at South West London and St George's Mental Health NHS Trust (2002) supported 81 people with mental health problems in existing clinical and non-clinical positions within the Trust on the same terms and conditions as everyone else.

Here are comments from two supported employees:

> Had it not existed then perhaps I wouldn't have got this job [...] now I'm a contributing member of society because of my employment here. Its worth is in altering the life of someone with mental illness [...] helping them to change direction from hopelessness to being worthwhile.
>
> I was walking around the grounds – drugged up and sick. Now I've come back down the road of no return with a different hat on and the User Employment Programme was part of the help and support that enabled me to do that.

A challenge for people who are returning to work – or asking professionals to support them in returning to work – is what Perkins (2001) calls professional negativity. Perkins, a psychologist who also has a diagnosis of manic depression and whom you met at the beginning of the course, was instrumental in setting up the user employment scheme described in Box 6.2. She argues:

> The hopelessness of mental health workers ensures that the services we provide are full of people who have 'given up' on themselves and their futures: a tragic waste of human lives and potential.
>
> But the presence of ongoing or recurring problems does not have to mean that our lives are over. Professionals may not be able to achieve the 'cures' to which they aspire – but recovery is possible. People can, and do, rebuild meaningful and valuable lives within and beyond the limits of disability.
>
> (Perkins, 2001, p. 6)

Peter Beresford, an academic who has also used mental health services, thinks that an integrated employment strategy is necessary to combat situations such as those he has experienced:

> I have seen mental health service users debarred from employment; facing discrimination because of problems dating from years before. I have seen them harried by benefits organisations, despite following all the rules to the letter, when they have obtained some small-scale paid work, which has increased their confidence, skills and self-esteem.
>
> I have watched service users wait in dread for the results of occupational health interviews after successful job applications. I've seen them routinely sidelined, denied promotion and confined to jobs far below their capabilities. I have been told dismissively by a psychiatrist that I might one day be able to get a job as a clerk. Most of all, we know about the grim association between poverty and mental health service use, related to the disproportionately high rates of unemployment among mental health service users – the highest for any group of disabled people. [...]

> Many mental health service users want to get back into paid work, but as a right, not an obligation. They want flexible employment, decent employment conditions, safeguards against discrimination, access to proper education, training and recognised qualifications and for their experience to be valued.
>
> They also want flexibility between benefits and work. [...] Policy makers have got to stop thinking in crude binary terms of can work, can't work. The reality is that many more survivors would be able to stay in employment if they were ensured the continuous and crisis support they may need.
>
> (Beresford, 2003, p. 20)

There are practical things that both employers and service users/survivors can do to can help the move into employment. A report called *Valuing Experience* (Gell, 2001) brought together experiences from people who have used mental health services. One aim of the report was to be an inspiration and aid to people in thinking about reclaiming their citizenship, by getting involved in mental health services and training schemes as an 'expert by experience'. Another was to help inform and enable employers in supporting service users/survivors. The key messages are outlined in Box 6.3.

Box 6.3 Key messages about involvement and employment

Key messages for 'experts by experience'

Think about the role before you take it on

- Is it a role where you can be yourself?
- Is it with people you will feel comfortable with?
- Will it be an isolated role, or will there be supportive colleagues?
- Do you want to start in a voluntary capacity to try it out?
- Are there manageable boundaries to the role?
- Can you identify your support and training needs before you start work?
- Have you thought through any implications and got advice, for instance with self-employment, or with benefit entitlements?

Then, if it appeals to you, go for it!

- Have faith in your abilities.
- Look at your experiences differently. Think of the skills and expertise you have gained. Take a rational perspective.
- Get feedback from interviews if you do not get the job.
- Don't worry. Don't be afraid. Don't give up.

Value yourself! Look after yourself!

- Don't let people take your expertise for granted.
- Claim your expenses or appropriate pay. You are not a charity.
- If you are not satisfied with your conditions at work, ask for change.
- Be assertive rather than aggressive.
- Know your rights. Join a trade union or make sure you have a similar type or level of support.
- Make sure your support and training needs are being addressed.
- Take up new challenges that interest you, don't confine yourself to mental health issues.

You can make a difference ...

[...]

Key messages for managers

Value the expertise that survivors and service users bring

- Pay them appropriately.
- Employ them in permanently funded positions.
- Build user posts into new services from the start.
- Provide the support and training required.
- Ensure their status within the workforce reflects their expertise.
- Promote a culture amongst staff that respects this status and accepts change.

Support survivors and service users, and meet individual needs

- A supportive manager is crucial to avoid the worker being marginalised.
- Pay for outside supervision from someone of the postholder's choice.
- Set up regular weekly supervision by the immediate line manager.
- Arrange regular meetings with other employed service users.

For service users attending committees

- Cover expenses and pay for attendance.
- Provide training on structures, systems, procedures and jargon.
- Support and link in representatives with the wider user community.

For volunteers

- Cover expenses and give advice on benefit regulations.
- Provide support and training as required; promote teamwork.
- Provide an agreement which sets out the responsibilities of both parties.
- Ensure the work does not spiral out of control.
- Voluntary work should benefit the volunteer, and not put him or her at risk.

(Source: Gell, 2001, pp. 56–9)

What does this kind of involvement feel like? In the final activity in this unit you listen to Abina Parshad-Griffin, who thinks that citizenship can be promoted and exclusion challenged by service user involvement.

Activity 6.5 **Involving citizens?**

30 minutes

Learning outcome 4

Parshad-Griffin has a great deal of experience of service user involvement projects and initiatives and sees them as a means of establishing citizenship. Listen to track 6 of Audio 1 and make some notes on the key points she makes and the challenges she identifies.

Comment

A course tester who works in social services commented:

> I think Abina's contribution is one of the strongest in the course so far – in particular, her experience and feelings of tokenism, within user involvement panels, and what she had to say about a hierarchy of diagnosis.

> Professional fear of working with her due to her high profile is interesting. I can understand this to a certain extent. The blame culture can contribute to defensive working practices. I can understand then why Abina found it difficult to get support when she most needed it.
>
> It is also very easy for our managers to say 'we are working towards' something, without actually deciding how you are going to achieve it. I sometimes see it as window dressing. I do not doubt the sincerity of those working in the field on an individual level, but I am suspicious of new initiatives when they are delivered from above without proper consultation with users and staff.

Another course tester who has both used and worked in mental health services focused on what Parshad-Griffin has to say about user involvement, especially the 'empty chair' she insists on, to remind people of service users/survivors whose voices are not heard.

Parshad-Griffin identifies and discusses many challenges related to user involvement and citizenship. On the one hand it can result in better services and practices, and at its best will take place at all levels, or, as she says, 'at the point of contact, care and congress'. On the other, she expresses concern about the boundaries and hierarchies that are developing within service user/survivor movements, and especially about people who have no choice when it comes to their identity and lifestyle. Throughout this unit, and indeed throughout Module 1, you have seen how important identity is, and how important it is to look at it holistically. Parshad-Griffin was asked to facilitate a workshop for the Mental Health Act Commission and wrote about her experiences as follows:

> They may want the black and minority ethnic part of me, they may want the woman part of me, they may even want the mental health service user part of me, but they do not want the 'underclass benefits' part of me [...] You see, the problem is I don't come in parts – all of me or none of me!
>
> (Parshad-Griffin, 2000, p. 13)

6 Conclusion

We began this unit with a quotation about the importance of tackling exclusion and discrimination at all levels and in all aspects of our lives. Social exclusion presents some profound challenges to everyone involved with mental health services at whatever level. You have explored the possibility of employment as a strategy likely to promote inclusion. Rufus May talked about 'personal wisdom' and how it might be of benefit to people working in mental health; Peter Beresford argued for access to all forms of employment for people who have had mental health problems. But is work the only answer? There will always be those for whom it is not appropriate or possible. Are there other ways that people might move into meaningful occupation? Another way might be to use 'personal wisdom' and become an expert by experience.

Whichever way you decide to tackle discrimination, it is not only, as Sayce argues, at the wider, institutional level that inclusion and exclusion take place. The identity of citizen may be compromised by a psychiatric diagnosis and the subsequent actions and responses of others. It is, therefore, crucially important that as active citizens we all respond to counter discrimination and exclusion.

References

Beresford, P. (2003) 'On the way to work', *Community Care*, 19–25 June, p. 20.

Bracken, P. (2003) *Citizenship and Psychiatry*, paper presented at inaugural seminar, Centre for Citizenship and Community Mental Health, University of Bradford.

Department for Social Security (1998) *New Ambitions for our Century: A New Contract for Welfare*, Cm 3805, London, The Stationery Office.

Department of Health (1999) *The National Service Framework for Mental Health: Modern Standards and Service Models*, London, DH.

Gell, C. (2001) *Valuing Experience*, London, Kings College London.

Goffman, E. (1990) *Stigma: Notes on the Management of Spoiled Identity*, 2nd edition, Harmondsworth, Penguin.

Home Office (1998) *Speaking up for Justice: Report of the Inter-departmental Working Group on the Treatment of Vulnerable or Intimidated Witnesses in the Criminal Justice System*, London, Home Office.

Huxley, P. and Thornicroft, G. (2003) 'Social inclusion, social quality and mental illness', *British Journal of Psychiatry*, Vol. 182, pp. 289–90.

Ignatieff, M. (1989) 'Citizenship and moral narcissism', *The Political Quarterly*, Vol. 60, pp. 63–74.

Lombardo, P. (1983) 'Involuntary sterilization in Virginia: from Buck v. Bell to Poe v. Lynchburg', *Developments in Mental Health Law*, Vol. 3, No. 3, pp. 17–21.

Mental Health Foundation (2000) *Pull Yourself Together!* London, MHF.

Miller, C. (2000) 'Citizenship and inclusion', *Openmind*, Vol. 105, Sept/Oct, pp. 10–11.

Mowbray, C.T., Oyersman, D., Zemencuk, J.K. and Ross, S.R. (1995) 'Motherhood for women with serious mental illness', *American Journal of Orthopsychiatry*, Vol. 65, No. 1, pp. 21–38.

NSF Scotland (2001) *Give us a Break*, Edinburgh, NSF Scotland.

Office for National Statistics (1999) *Labour Force Survey 1997/8*, London, ONS.

Page, S. (1977) 'Effects of the mental illness label in attempts to obtain accommodation', *Canadian Journal of Behavioral Sciences*, Vol. 9, pp. 85–90.

Parshad-Griffin, A. (2000) 'Divide and cruel', *Openmind*, Vol. 105, Sept/Oct, p. 13.

Perkins, R. (2001) 'The "you'll nevers"', *Openmind*, Vol. 107, Jan/Feb, p. 6.

Pilgrim, D. and Rogers, A. (1999) *A Sociology of Mental Health and Illness* 2nd edition, Buckingham, Open University Press.

Read, J. and Baker, S. (1996) *Not Just Sticks and Stones: A Survey of the Stigma, Taboos and Discrimination Experienced by People with Mental Health Problems*, London, Mind.

Repper, J., Sayce, L., Strong, S., Willmot, J. and Haines, M. (1997) *Tall Stories from the Back Yard: A Survey of Nimby Opposition to Community Mental Health Facilities Experienced by Key Service Providers in England and Wales*, London, Mind.

Sainsbury Centre for Mental Health (2002) *Briefing 15: An Executive Briefing on 'Working for Inclusion'*, London, SCMH.

Sayce, L. (2000) *From Psychiatric Patient to Citizen: Overcoming Discrimination and Social Exclusion*, Basingstoke, Macmillan Press.

Sayce, L. and Measey, L. (1999) 'Strategies to reduce social exclusion for people with mental health problems', *Psychiatric Bulletin*, Vol. 23, No. 2, pp. 65–7.

Social Exclusion Unit (2001) 'Welcome to the Social Exclusion Unit', www.socialexclusionunit.gov.uk [accessed 05/02/04].

South West London and St George's Mental Health NHS Trust (2002) *User Employment Scheme, Progress Report.*

Stefan, S. (1989) 'Whose egg is it anyway? Reproductive rights of incarcerated, institutionalised and incompetent women', *Nova Law Review*, Vol. 13, No. 2, pp. 406–56.

United States Holocaust Memorial Museum (1996) *Handicapped*, Washington, DC, United States Holocaust Memorial Museum.

Acknowledgements

Grateful acknowledgement is made to the following sources for permission to reproduce material in this module:

Unit 2

Text

Page 35: Perkins, R. 'On the questions of genes ...', *Openmind*, 120, Mar./Apr. 2003, © 2003 Mind (National Association for Mental Health), reprinted with permission.

Artwork

Figure 2.1: based on Sinton, J. *Spirituality and Mental Health Care: Rediscovering a 'Forgotten' Dimension*, Jessica Kingsley Publishers; cartoon, page 7: 'The genetic theory of schizophrenia', by Séan Terrell, *Openmind*, 97, May/June 1999, © 1999 Mind (National Association for Mental Health), reprinted with permission.

Unit 3

Figure 3.1: Maslow, A. *Motivation and Personality*, 1st edition, © 1954, reproduced by permission of Pearson Education, Inc., Upper Saddle River, New Jersey.

Unit 4

Figure 4.1: Papadopoulos, I., Tilki, M. and Taylor, G. (1998) *Transcultural Care: A Guide for Health Care Professionals*, Mark Allen Publishing Ltd, reproduced by permission.

Unit 5

Table 5.1: Harrison, A. (2002) 'Somatisation', *Mental Health Practice*, Vol. 4, No. 6, RCN Publishing.

Unit 6

Text

Poem, page 131: '20th Century Values', based on the words of Pastor Martin Niemoller, with permission from Sibylle Sarah Niemoller von Sell; pages 143–4: Beresford, P. 'On the way to work', *Community Care*, 19–25 June 2003, Elsevier Science.

Artwork

Page 134: 'Lost in the benefits jungle', © 2004 Mind (The National Association for Mental Health), reprinted with permission; Figure 6.1: Bracken, P. *Seminar Paper – Citizenship and Psychiatry*, 26 June 2003, © 2003 Dr P. Bracken, reproduced with permission.

Every effort has been made to contact copyright owners. If any have been inadvertently overlooked, the publishers will be pleased to make the necessary arrangements at the first opportunity.